Balanced Assessment for the Mathematics Curriculum

HIGH SCHOOL
ASSESSMENT

■

BERKELEY
HARVARD
MICHIGAN STATE
SHELL CENTRE

PACKAGE H2

Pre-publication Unit

Dale Seymour Publications®

Project Directors: Alan Schoenfeld
                     Hugh Burkhardt
                     Phil Daro
                     Jim Ridgway
                     Judah Schwartz
                     Sandra Wilcox

Managing Editor: Alan MacDonell
Acquisitions Editor: Merle Silverman
Production/Manufacturing Director: Janet Yearian
Senior Production Coordinator: Fiona Santoianni
Design Director: Phyllis Aycock
Design Manager: Jeff Kelly

The work of this project was supported by a grant from the National Science Foundation. The opinions expressed in these materials do not necessarily represent the position, policy, or endorsement of the Foundation.

This book is published by Dale Seymour Publications®,
an imprint of Addison Wesley Longman, Inc.

Dale Seymour Publications
10 Bank Street
White Plains, NY 10602-5026
Customer Service: 800-872-1100

Printed in the United States of America.

Order number 33008
ISBN 0-7690-0071-1

1 2 3 4 5 6 7 8 9 10 - SG - 02 01 00 99 98

Authors

This assessment package was designed and developed by members of the Balanced Assessment Project team, particularly Jana Branissa, Joanne Lobato, Susan Dean, Manuel Santos, Alan Schoenfeld, Ann Shannon, Dick Stanley and Malcolm Swan, Marion Walter, Dan Zimmerlin. The coordinator was Ann Shannon.

Many others have made helpful comments and suggestions in the course of the development. We thank them all. The project is particularly grateful to the teachers and students with whom these tasks were developed and tested,
The project was directed by Alan Schoenfeld, Hugh Burkhardt, Phil Daro, Jim Ridgway, Judah Schwartz and Sandra Wilcox.

The package consists of materials compiled or adapted from work done at the four sites of the Balanced Assessment Project:

Balanced Assessment
Graduate School of Education
University of California
Berkeley, CA 94720-1670
USA

Balanced Assessment
Educational Technology Center
Harvard University
Cambridge, MA 02138
USA

Balanced Assessment (MARS)
513 Erickson Hall
Michigan State University
East Lansing, MI 48824
USA

Balanced Assessment
Shell Centre for Mathematical Education
University of Nottingham
Nottingham NG7 2RD
England

Additional tasks and packages, the materials in their original form, and other assessment resources such as guides to scoring may be obtained from the project sites. For a full list of available publications, and for further information, contact any of the sites or the Project's Mathematics Assessment Resource Services at the Michigan State address above.

Introduction

What is Balanced Assessment? . . . What is Balance? . . . Dimensions of Balance . . . What's in a Package? . . . What's included with each task? . . . Scoring Student Work

Using this package

Expanded Table of Contents

For More Information

The Tasks

Glossary

What is Balanced Assessment?

Mathematics assessments tell us and our students how well they are learning mathematics. A carefully designed mathematics assessment should:

- assess the mathematics that counts, focusing on important ideas and processes;

- be fair to the students, providing them with a set of opportunities to demonstrate what they know and can do;

- be fair to the curriculum, offering a balance of opportunities - long and short tasks, basic knowledge and problem solving, individual and group work, and the spectrum of concepts and processes that reflect the vision of the *Standards;*

- be of such high quality that students and teachers learn from them - so that assessment time serves as instructional time, and assessment and curriculum live in harmony;

- provide useful information to administrators, so they can judge the effectiveness of their programs; to teachers, so they can judge the quality of their instruction; and to students and parents, so they can see where the students are doing well and where work is needed.

This is such an assessment package, dealing with the mathematics appropriate for the middle grades. It was designed by the Balanced Assessment Project, an NSF-supported collaboration that was funded to create a series of exemplary assessment items and packages for assessing students' mathematical performance at various grade levels (elementary, middle school, high school, and "senior" or grade 12). Balanced Assessment offers a wide range of extensively field-tested tasks and packages - some paper-and-pencil, some high-tech or multimedia - and consulting services to help states and districts implement meaningful and informative mathematics assessments.

What is Balance?

It's easy to see what isn't balanced. An assessment that focuses on computation only is out of balance. So is one that focuses on algebra, patterns, and function to the exclusion of geometry, shape, and space, or that ignores or gives a cursory nod toward statistics and probability. Likewise, assessments that do not provide students with ample opportunity to show how they can reason or communicate mathematically are unbalanced. These are content and process dimensions of balance, but there are many others - length of task, whether tasks are pure or applied, and so on. Table 1 shows some of the dimensions used to design and balance this package.

Dimensions of Balance

Mathematical Content Dimension

- **Mathematical content** will include some of:

    Number and Quantity including: concepts and representation; computation; estimation and measurement; number theory and general number properties.

    Algebra, Patterns and Function including: patterns and generalization; functional relationships (including ratio and proportion); graphical and tabular representation; symbolic representation; forming and solving relationships.

    Geometry, Shape and Space including: shape, properties of shapes, relationships; spatial representation, visualization and construction; location and movement; transformation and symmetry; trigonometry.

    Handling Data, Statistics and Probability including: collecting, representing, interpreting data; probability models – experimental and theoretical; simulation.

    Other Mathematics including: discrete mathematics, including combinatorics; underpinnings of calculus; mathematical structures.

Mathematical Process Dimension

- **Phases** of problem solving, reasoning and communication will include, as broad categories, some or all of:

    Modeling and Formulating;
    Transforming and Manipulating;
    Inferring and Drawing Conclusions;
    Checking and Evaluating;
    Reporting.

Task Type Dimensions

- **Task Type** will be one of: open investigation; non-routine problem; design; plan; evaluation and recommendation; review and critique; re-presentation of information; technical exercise; definition of concepts.

- **Non-routineness** in: context; mathematical aspects or results; mathematical connections.

- **Openness**: it may have an open end with open questions; open middle.

- **Type of Goal** is one of: pure mathematics; illustrative application of the mathematics; applied power over the practical situation.

- ***Reasoning Length*** *is the expected time for the longest section of the task (It is an indication of the amount of 'scaffolding' – the detailed step-by-step guidance that the prompt may provide)*

Circumstances of Performance Dimensions

- **Task Length**: ranging from short tasks (5-15 minutes), through long tasks (15-60 minutes), to extended tasks (several days to several weeks)

- **Modes of Presentation**: written; oral; video; computer.

- **Modes of Working** on the task: individual; group; mixed.

- **Modes of Response** by the student: written; built; spoken; programmed; performed.

Table 1

What's in a Package?

A typical Balanced Assessment Package offers ten to twenty "tasks", ranging in "length" from 5 to 45 minutes. Some of the tasks consist of a single problem, while others consist of a sequence of problems. Taken together, the tasks provide students with an opportunity to display their knowledge and skills across the broad spectrum of content and processes described in the *Standards.* To put things bluntly, you can't get this kind of rich information with less assessment time – but it's worth it, for the problems are mathematically rich and well worth the time spent on them. You can get more information, and you should if possible – for example with portfolios including samples of extended student project work.

What's included with each task?

We have tried to provide you with as much information as possible about the mathematics that is central to solving a task, about managing the assessment, and about typical student responses and how to analyze the mathematics in them. Each section of this package, corresponding to one task, consists of the following:

Overview

The first page of each section provides a quick overview that lets you see whether the task is appropriate for use at any particular point in the curriculum. This overview includes:

- Task Description - the situation that students will be asked to investigate or solve;

- Assumed Mathematical Background - the kinds of previous experiences students will need to have had to engage the task productively;

- Core Elements of Performance - the mathematical ideas and processes that are central to the task;

- Circumstances of Performance - the estimated time for students to work on the task, the special materials that the task requires, whether students work individually, in pairs or in small groups, and any other such information.

Task Prompt

The task prompt begins with a statement for the student characterizing the aims of the task. In some cases there is a pre-assessment activity that teachers assign in advance of the formal assessment. In some cases there is a launch activity that familiarizes students with the context but is not part of the formal assessment. All such activities are included in this section.

Sample Solution

Each task is accompanied by at least one solution; where there are multiple approaches to a problem, we may provide more than one.

Using the Task

Here we provide suggestions about launching the task and helping students understand the context of the problem. Some tasks have pre-activities; some have students do some initial exploration in pairs or as a whole class to become familiar with the context while the formal assessment is done individually. Such suggestions are discussed here. Information from field-testing about aspects of tasks that students may find challenging is given here. We may also include suggestions for subsequent classroom instruction related to the task, as well as possible extensions that can be used for assessment or instructional purposes.

Characterizing Student Performance

This section contains descriptions of characteristic student responses that the task is likely to elicit. These descriptions, based on the Core Elements of Performance, indicate various levels of successful engagement with the task. They are accompanied by annotated artists' renderings of typical student work. These illustrations of student work will prepare you to assess the wide range of responses produced by your students. We have chosen examples that show something of the range and variety of responses to the task, and the various aspects of mathematical performance it calls for. The commentary is intended to exemplify these key aspects of performance at various levels across several domains. Teachers and others have found both the examples and the commentary extremely useful; its purpose is to bring out explicitly for each task the wide range of aspects of mathematical performance which the standards imply.

Scoring Student Work

The discussions of student work in the section "Characterizing Student Performance" are deliberately qualitative and non-technical; they are designed to focus on the mathematical ideas that "count." We need more – we need reliable and informative scoring methods. One thing should be clear: just saying "Johnny got a 75" is *not* informative, for it tells us little about what Johnny knew or didn't know, in order to be assigned a score of 75. Hence we must report in more scope, and in more detail. There is no "one size fits all" scoring method. Different methods have different emphases, and different strengths. Recognizing that diversity, we have developed a range of approaches and scoring rubrics. For example, a *holistic rubric* describes four levels of performance. This is not a generic rubric but is written specifically for each individual task. A *holistic-within-category rubric* describes four levels of performance for each of the following: problem solving and reasoning; mathematical content (the five main content areas in our dimensions for balance); communication (if there is a specified audience). A *point rubric* assigns points for specific parts of the task, partitioned among the same headings (content, process, communication). *Dual scoring* combines point scoring of detail with the overall view of a holistic rubric. An *object x action rubric* assigns points for modeling and formulating, transforming and manipulating, inferring and drawing conclusions, and communicating with respect to the content domain of the task.

These schemes are developed in separate Scoring Guides. They can be used as is, or modified or adapted to your needs.

Using this package

This assessment package may be used in a variety of ways, depending on your local needs and circumstances.

- You may want to implement formal performance assessment under controlled conditions at the school, district or state level. This package provides a balanced set of tasks appropriate for such on-demand, high stakes assessment.

- You may want to provide opportunities for classroom-based performance assessment, embedded within the curriculum, under less controlled conditions. This package allows teachers the discretion of selecting tasks that are appropriate for use at particular points in the curriculum.

- You may be looking for tasks to serve as a transition toward a curriculum as envisioned in the *Standards* or as enrichment for existing curriculum. In this case, the tasks in this package can serve as rich instructional problems to enhance your curriculum. They are exemplars of the kinds of instructional tasks that will support performance assessment and can be used for preparing students for future performance assessment. Even in these situations, the tasks provide teachers with rich sites to engage in informal assessment of student understanding.

Preparing for the assessment

We urge teachers to work through a task themselves before giving it to their students. This gives teachers an opportunity to become familiar with the context and the mathematical demands of the task, and to anticipate what might need to be highlighted in launching the task.

It is important to have at hand all the necessary materials students need to engage a task before launching them on the task. We assume that students have certain tools and materials available at all times in the mathematics classroom and that these will be accessible to students to choose from during any assessment activity.

At the middle grades these resources include

- grid paper and square and isometric dot paper;
- dice, square tiles, cubes and other concrete materials;
- calculators;
- rulers, compasses, and protractors or angle rulers;
- scissors, markers, tape, string, paper clips and glue.

If a task requires any special materials, these are specified in the task.

Managing the assessment

We anticipate that this package will be used in a variety of situations. Therefore, our guidance about managing assessment is couched in fairly general suggestions. We signal some considerations you will likely want to take into account under various circumstances.

The way in which any particular task is introduced to students will vary. The launch will be shaped by a number of considerations (e.g., the students, the complexity of the instructions, the degree of familiarity students have with the context of the problem). In some cases it will be necessary only to distribute the task to students and then let them read and work through the task. Other situations may call for the teacher to read the task to the class to assure that everyone understands the instructions, the context, and the aim of the assessment. Decisions of this kind will be influenced by the age of the students, their experiences with reading mathematical tasks, their fluency with English, whether difficulties in reading would exclude them from otherwise productively engaging with the mathematics of the task.

Under conditions of formal assessment, once students have been set to work on a task, the teacher should not intervene except where specified. This is essential in formal, high stakes assessment but it is important under any assessment circumstance. Even the slightest intervention by the teacher – reinterpreting instructions, suggesting ways to begin, offering prompts when students appear to be stuck – has the potential to significantly alter the task for the student. However, teachers should provide general encouragement within a supportive classroom environment as a normal part of doing mathematics in school. This includes reminding students about the aim of the assessment (using the words at the beginning of the task prompt), when the period of assessment is nearing an end, and how to turn in their work when they have completed the task.

We suggest a far more relaxed use of the package when students are meeting these kinds of tasks for the first time, particularly in situations where they are being used primarily as learning tasks to enhance the curriculum. Under these circumstances teachers may reasonably decide to do some coaching, talk with students as they work on a task, pose questions when they seem to get stuck. In these instances the teacher may be using the tasks for informal assessment – observing what strategies students favor, what kinds of questions they ask, what they seem to understand and what they are struggling with, what kinds of prompts get them unstuck. This can be extremely useful information in helping the teacher make ongoing instructional and assessment decisions. However, as students have more experiences with these kinds of tasks, the amount of coaching by the teacher should decline and students should rely less on this kind of assistance.

Under conditions of formal assessment, you will need to make decisions about how tasks will be scored and by whom, how scores will be aggregated across tasks, and how students' accomplishments will be reported to interested constituencies. The Scoring Guide which accompanies this package provides some guidance about these matters. However, these decisions will, of necessity, be made at the school, district or state level and will likely reflect educational, political and economic considerations specific to the local context.

Expanded Table of Contents

	Task Type	Circumstances of Performance
Chocolate polyhedra Task 6010	45 minute pure investigation, with some non-routine aspects of mathematics in a non-routine context; open-ended	individual assessment; written prompt and response
Ordering a cab Task 6020	45 minute recommendation task; applied power in a non-routine context from student life	individual assessment; written prompt and response
Sort them Task 6030	45 minute problem in pure mathematics, involving a non-routine approach to connecting 4 different representations of functions	discussion in pairs, with individual written responses
House in a hurry Task 6040	45 minute planning, involving applied power over a non-routine context from adult life; it is open-ended, allowing significantly different solutions	discussion in pairs, with individual written responses
Checking an odometer Task 6050	45 minute problem; illustrative application of proportional reasoning in a non-routine context from student life	individual assessment; written prompt and response
Design a tent Task 6060	45 minute design task; applied power in a non-routine context from student life	individual assessment, perhaps after class explanation; individual written responses
2500% Blowup Task 6070	45 minute problem; illustrative application of proportional reasoning in a non-routine context from student life	discussion in pairs, with individual written responses

Mathematical Content	Mathematical Processes
Geometry, Shape and Space: properties of sections of a cube by various mid-planes; strong visualization demand; investigation of Euler's formula for polyhedra, in this context and beyond	formulation of the problem is the main challenge, with interpretation and evaluation of the results important for checking.
Data, Statistics and Probability: choice and use of appropriate representations of data for analysis of the response times of cabs; construction of competing arguments	representation, interpretation and evaluation of the data; formulation and communication of the arguments
Algebra, Pattern and Functions: sorting and connecting the tabular, algebraic, graphical and verbal representations of 10 simple functions	interpretation of the given representations, based on understanding of the transformations between them.
Other Mathematics: the discrete mathematics of scheduling jobs, successively and in parallel, is approached informally; student must devise and use appropriate charts and diagrams	formulation of a systematic approach to the problem; manipulation of the given data; interpretation, evaluation and communication of the results
Algebra, Pattern and Functions: recognizing the need for, and using proportional reasoning in relating an odometer which reads 15% low to the real distances; forward and reverse reasoning	formulating the model; transforming the data given in the various parts of the task
Geometry, Shape and Space, with Number: estimation of sizes of people and tent dimensions; visualizing shape of the net for the tent; Pythagorean Theorem and/or trigonometry for lengths, angles	formulating the estimates, and the net shape; manipulations for calculating the lengths and angles
Geometry, Shape and Space, with Number: proportional reasoning in a geometric situation, involving measurements on two enlarged photos, with inferences about the negative	formulating the approach; manipulations, both measurement and computation, inference about the negative

	Task Type	Circumstances of Performance
Kidney stones Task 6080	45 minute exercise on combining probabilities; adult life context; applied power	discussion in pairs, with individual written responses
Packaging a soda bottle Task 6090	60 minute design task; applied power; non-routine mathematical connections and adult life context	discussion in pairs, with individual written responses
The "Cross the box" game Task 6100	60 minute open investigation; applied power in a non-routine context from student life; open-ended	play the game in pairs; individual written responses
Wheelchair access Task 6110	45 minute design task; applied power in a non-routine context from student life; open-ended	individual assessment; written prompt and response

Mathematical Content	Mathematical Processes
Data, Statistics and Probability: combining probabilities by addition and multiplication, with circle chart	manipulation and interpretation of the data given, formulation of the standard method for combining probabilities
Geometry, Space and Shape, with Number: visualization of the form of the net for cuboid and hexagonal prism boxes; measurement of given figure; computation with Pythagorean Theorem	formulation of the approach; manipulation through measurement, calculation and sketching
Data, Statistics and Probability: probability distribution of the difference of two dice; collecting and analyzing data from such a game; inferring best strategy	manipulation in collecting and analyzing data, inference and formulation of a strategy for placing the cans
Geometry, Space and Shape, with Number: visualization of forms for the ramp; computation of slope constraints	formulation of possible designs; transformation of ramp constraints into dimensions; communicate the design and how it meets the conditions

For More Information

Additional information about this package, about a range of assessment issues, and about services offered by the Balanced Assessment Project and its consulting team, the *Mathematics Assessment Resource Service,* can be obtained by contacting any of the project sites listed on page 1. In addition to its extensive task and package collection, Balanced Assessment offers a number of technical and theoretical papers explaining the theoretical underpinnings of our work - e.g., a document entitled *A Framework for Balance,,* which provides the theoretical structure that underlies the "dimensions of Balance" in Table 1.

Glossary

Applied power over the practical situation: a task goal which is to provide the student an opportunity to demonstrate power over a real-world practical situation; it exemplifies the use of mathematics in the world outside school.

Checking and evaluating: a mathematical process that involves evaluating the quality of the solution in relation to the problem situation (e.g., checking calculations; comparing model predictions with data; considering whether solution is reasonable and appropriate; asking further questions).

Definition of concepts: a task type that requires the clarification of a concept or the generation of a definition to fit a set of conditions.

Design: a task type that calls for the design, and perhaps construction, of an object (e.g., a model building, a scale drawing, a game) together with instructions on how to use the object; may include evaluating the results in light of various constraints and desirable features.

Evaluation and recommendation: a task type that calls for collection and analysis of information bearing on a decision, a review of the evidence, and a proposed recommendation that is supported by the evidence; the product is a "consultant" report for a "client."

Illustrative application of mathematics: a task goal which is to provide the student an opportunity to demonstrate power over a situation in which the mathematics is linked to a context outside mathematics; the focus is on the specific piece of mathematics, the reality and utility of the context as a model of a practical situation is secondary.

Inferring and drawing conclusions: a mathematical process that involves applying the results of the manipulation to the original problem and interpreting the results in light of the problem situation.

Modeling and formulating: a mathematical process that involves taking the statement of the situation as presented in the task and formulating the problem to be solved; selecting appropriate representations to model the situation.

Non-routine problem: a task type that presents an unfamiliar problem situation that students are not expected to have analyzed before or have not met regularly in the curriculum; demands some flexibility of thinking, and adaptation or extension of

---

previous knowledge; may be situated in a *context* that students have not encountered in the curriculum; may involve introduction of *concepts and techniques* that will be explicitly taught at a later stage; may involve discovery of *connections* among mathematical ideas.

Open-end: a task structure in which a question is posed that can lead to multiple solutions and that allows for a variety of strategies for approaching the problem; provides the student with the widest range of possibilities for choosing and making decisions.

Open investigation: an open-ended task type that invites exploration of a problem situation with the aim of discovering and establishing facts and relationships; criteria of performance is based on exploring thoroughly, generalizing, justifying, explaining with clarity and economy.

Open-middle: a task structure in which the solution is closed but which allows for a variety of strategies for approaching the problem.

Plan: a task type that calls for the design of a sequence of activities or the plan of a schedule of events where time is an essential variable and where the need to organize the efforts of others is implied.

Pure mathematics: a task goal which is to provide the student an opportunity to demonstrate power over a situation within a mathematics "microworld;" may be an open investigation, a problem, or a technical exercise.

Reporting: a mathematical process that involves communicating to others what has been learned about the problem; explaining why the results follow from formulating the problem and manipulating the formalism; drawing conclusions about implications of the results.

Re-presentation of information: a task type that requires interpretation of information presented in one form and its translation to some different form (e.g., write a set of verbal directions that would allow a listener to reproduce a given geometric design; represent the information in a piece of text with a graphic).

Review and critique: a task type that involves reflection on curriculum materials (e.g., review a piece of student work, identify errors, make suggestions for revision, pose further questions; produce notes on a recently learned topic).

Scaffolding: the amount of detailed step-by-step guidance in a task prompt.

Technical exercise: a task type that requires only the application of a learned procedure or a "tool kit" of techniques (e.g., adding decimals; solving an equation); the product is simply an answer that is judged for accuracy.

Transforming and manipulating: a mathematical process that involves manipulating the mathematical forms in which the problem is expressed (e.g., dividing one fraction by another, making a geometric construction, solving equations, plotting graphs, finding the derivative of a function).

Chocolate polyhedra

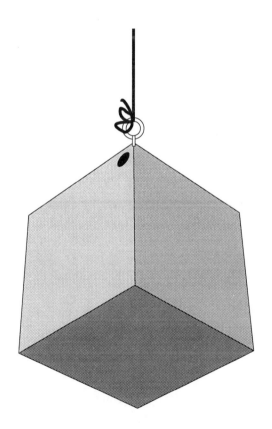

Chocolate polyhedra   *Overview*

Task Description

Grade Level: High

Students are asked to visualize the shape formed when
a cube half full of chocolate is left to set in different
positions. The task is a spatial reasoning one. Students
need to visualize and describe the shape.

At the end of the task students are given a part
statement of Euler's Formula for any polyhedra and
asked to use their work to figure out the complete
formula.

> *Visualize 3-D shapes.*
>
> *Sketch polyhedra.*
>
> *Explore Euler's Formula.*

Assumed Mathematical Background

Students should have had some experience working with 3-dimensional figures. It is expected
that all students will be familiar with the terms *face, vertex, and edge.*

Core Elements of Performance

The task provides students with the opportunity to:

- visualize 3-D shapes.
- sketch polyhedra.
- use Euler's Formula, (F) + (V) - (E) is equal to a certain number,
  to figure out the number.

Circumstances

Grouping: Students work individually.

Materials: A cube will be useful to students who have difficulty tackling this task.

Estimated time: 45 minutes

Acknowledgments

The idea for this task was developed in a conversation with Marion Walters.

Chocolate polyhedra

The aim of this assessment is to provide the opportunity for you to :
• *show how you can visualize 3-dimensional shapes.*
• *carry out an investigation.*

Imagine that you work in a chocolate factory and that you are responsible for designing interestingly shaped chocolates.

You have several plastic molds in the shape of a cube. They look like the one shown opposite.

Chocolate is poured into each mold through the small hole so that when set the mold is exactly half full.

To make different shaped chocolates, the molds are left to set in different positions.

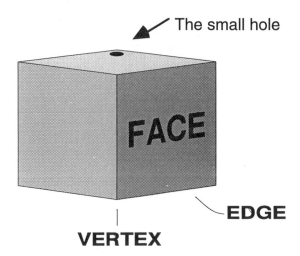

Each of the diagrams on the next page shows the position that the mold was left to set.

Look at each of the following diagrams.
- Make a sketch of the chocolate piece that is made.
- Record the number of faces that it has.
- Record the number of corners.
- Record the number of edges.
- Describe, as fully as possible, the shape that is made.

1.   *The mold sets while resting on one face.*

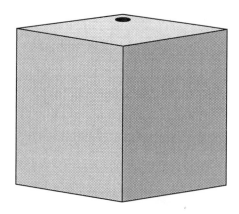

2.   *The mold sets while balanced perfectly on one edge at an angle of 45° to the horizontal.*

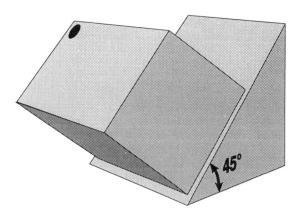

3.   *The mold sets while tilted on one edge at an angle of 20° to the horizontal.*

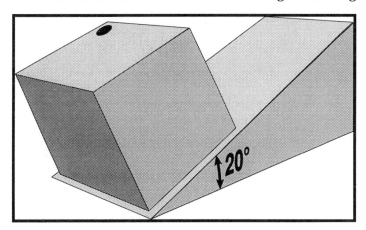

4.   *The mold sets while balanced perfectly on one vertex.*

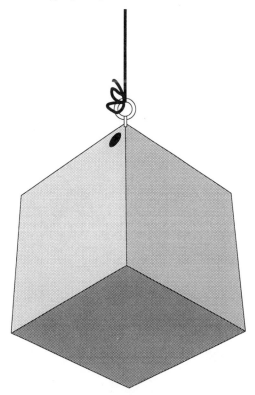

A Sample Solution

Position	number of faces	number of corners	number of edges
1. resting on a face	6	8	12
2. resting on an edge (45°)	5	6	9
3. resting on an edge (200°)	6	8	12
4. resting on one vertex	7	10	15

5.   The number is 2

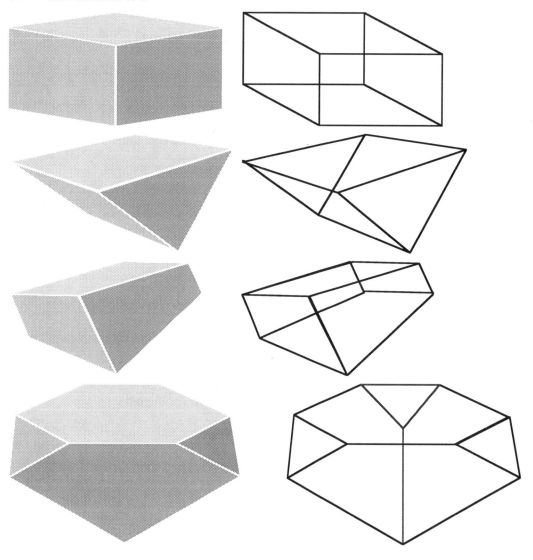

Extensions

Euler's Formula says that for any polyhedra:

> the number of faces (F) + the number of vertices (V) - the number of edges (E)
> is equal to a certain number.

Devise and report an investigation of this formula. Find out what that certain number is. You may use this work or any example of polyhedra. Packaging, especially those used for chocolate boxes are a good source. In your report include interesting polyhedra that illustrate Euler's Formula.

For Formal Assessment

Students usually find question 4 challenging. A clear cube that is half full of salt may be necessary to enable students to 'see' the correct solution.

This section offers a characterization of student responses and provides indications of the ways in which the students were successful or unsuccessful in engaging with and completing the task. The descriptions are keyed to the Core Elements of Performance. Our global descriptions of student work range from, "The student needs significant instruction," to, " The student's work meets the essential demands of the task." Samples of student work that exemplify these descriptions of performance are included below, accompanied by commentary on central aspects of each student's response. These sample responses are *representative*; they may not mirror the global description of performance in all respects, being weaker in some and stronger in others.

The characterization of student responses for this task is based on these Core Elements of Performance:

- visualize 3-D shapes.

- sketch polyhedra.

- use Euler's Formula, (F) + (V) - (E) is equal to a certain number,
  to figure out the number.

Descriptions of student work

The student needs significant instruction

These papers show, at most, evidence of clear understanding of what the task is asking. Typically the student might attempt the first part but might do so with little success.

Student A

This response shows that the student has attempted to engage with the task but has found it difficult to visualize and/or communicate the most straightforward situation.

The student needs some instruction

These papers provide evidence that the student can visualize and communicate the relatively straightforward situations.

Typically the response will provide the correct solution for the 1st and 2nd orientation.

Student B

This response shows that the student can visualize and communicate 3-dimensional shapes in relatively uncomplicated situations.

The student's work needs to be revised

The student will have completed the first three orientations correctly, and completed Euler's formula

Student C

This response shows that the student can visualize and communicate 3-dimensional shapes. It is expected that in a revision of this paper the student will complete Euler's formula and devise a way of visualizing the 4th orientation.

The student's work meets the essential demands of the task

The 4th orientation is exceptionally difficult and it is expected that few students will give the correct solution in an on-demand setting. Therefore, a response could score 4, without providing a correct solution to the 4th orientation. It is expected that all other aspects of the response will be correct.

Student D

This response shows that the student can visualize, and communicate 3-dimensional shapes.

With the exception of the 4th orientation, all aspect of the response are correct.

Student A

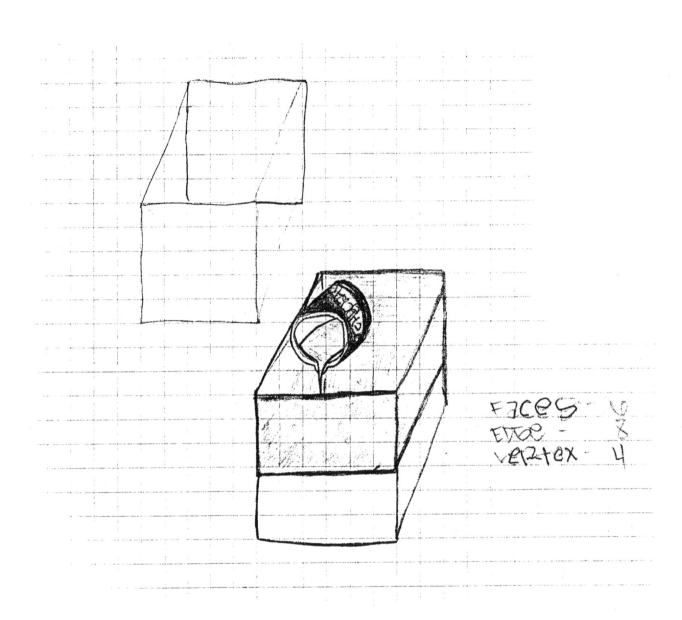

faces   4
edge -   8
vertex - 4

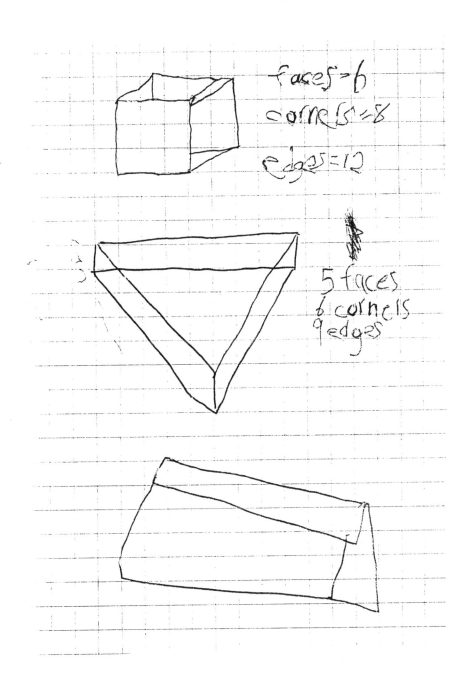

faces=6
corners=8
edges=12

5 faces
6 corners
9 edges

Student C

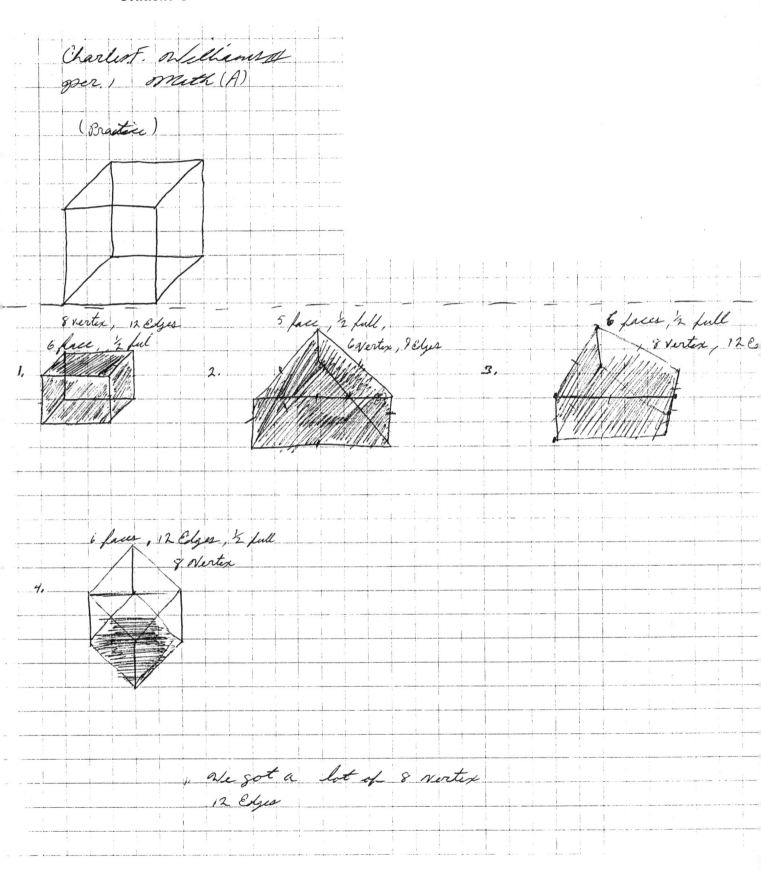

Charles F. Williams
per. 1   Smith (A)

(Practice)

8 vertex, 12 Edges

1.
6 face, ½ ful
8 vertex, 12 Edges

2.
5 face, ½ full,
6 vertex, 9 Edges

3.
6 faces, ½ full
8 vertex, 12 E.

4.
6 faces, 12 Edges, ½ full
8 Vertex

We got a lot of 8 vertex
12 Edges

Student D

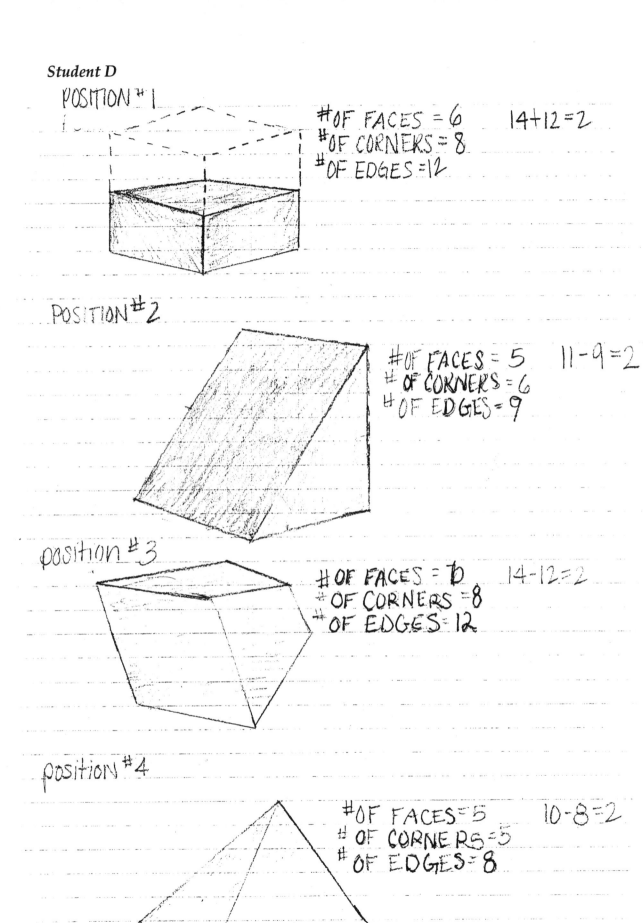

POSITION #1

#OF FACES = 6   14+12=2
#OF CORNERS = 8
#OF EDGES =12

POSITION #2

#OF FACES = 5   11-9=2
OF CORNERS = 6
OF EDGES = 9

position #3

OF FACES = 10   14-12=2
OF CORNERS = 8
OF EDGES = 12

position #4

#OF FACES=5   10-8=2
OF CORNERS=5
OF EDGES=8

Hi, I need a cab to pick me up at 7:00 am tomorrow....

Task Description

Grade Level: High

Students compare two taxicab companies on the basis of their punctuality. This involves the analysis of a considerable amount of raw data.

Students are involved in drawing graphs, calculating means, ranges, etc., and then in presenting reasoned cases in favor of each company in turn.

> *Represent data.*
>
> *Analyze data.*
>
> *Choose and use measures of central tendency and spread.*
>
> *Present opposing reasoned cases based on the same evidence.*
>
> *Evaluate the reasoning.*

Assumed Mathematical Background

Students should have had some experience of analyzing raw data using graphs and using measures of central tendency (mean, median and mode), spread (range, standard deviation), and developing an argument based on their findings.

Core Elements of Performance

- Choose and use appropriate measures to analyze and compare two sets of data.
- Choose and use appropriate graphs and/or diagrams to represent and analyze these data.
- Present opposing reasoned cases from the same data.
- Evaluate the reasoning and selecting the best case.

Circumstances

Grouping: Students work individually or in pairs. Pair work should encourage discussion. Each member of a pair, however, must produce his or her own written solution.

Materials: Each student will need graph paper or squared paper and a calculator. They may also ask for a protractor (if they wish to draw a pie chart).

Estimated time: 45 minutes

Ordering a cab

The aim of this assessment is to provide the opportunity for you to:
- *choose and use appropriate calculations to analyze data.*
- *choose and use appropriate graphs and/or diagrams to analyze data.*
- *reason clearly and convincingly.*

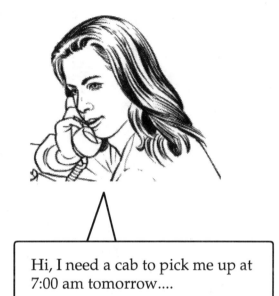

Hi, I need a cab to pick me up at 7:00 am tomorrow....

Sunshine cabs and Bluebird cabs are rival companies.
Each claims that their cab company is better than the other.

Sarah has to take a cab to work each day.
She wants to compare the two companies.

Over several months Sarah orders each cab 20 times.
She records how early or late they are when arriving to pick her up from her home.

Her results are shown on the next page.

Sunshine cabs		Bluebird cabs	
3 mins 30 secs	Early	3 mins 45 secs	Late
45 secs	Late	4 mins 30 secs	Late
1 min 30 secs	Late	3 mins	Late
4 mins 30 secs	Late	5 mins	Late
45 secs	Early	2 mins 15 secs	Late
2 mins 30 secs	Early	2 mins 30 secs	Late
4 mins 45 secs	Late	1 min 15 secs	Late
2 mins 45 secs	Late	45 secs	Late
30 secs	Late	3 mins	Late
1 minute 30 secs	Early	30 secs	Early
2 mins 15 secs	Late	1 min 30 secs	Late
9 mins 15 secs	Late	3 mins 30 secs	Late
3 mins 30 secs	Late	6 mins	Late
1 min 15 secs	Late	4 mins 30 secs	Late
30 secs	Early	5 mins 30 secs	Late
2 mins 30 secs	Late	2 mins 30 secs	Late
30 secs	Late	4 mins 15 secs	Late
7 mins 15 secs	Late	2 mins 45 secs	Late
5 mins 30 secs	Late	3 mins 45 secs	Late
3 mins	Late	4 mins 45 secs	Late

1. At the moment, it is hard to see which company is better.
   Use appropriate calculations, graphs and/or diagrams to analyze these data so that comparisons are easier to make.
   Show step-by-step what you did.

2. Present a reasoned case for Sunshine cabs being the better company.
   Present your reasoning as fully and as clearly as possible.

3. Present a reasoned case for Bluebird cabs being the better company.

4. Which argument do you think is more convincing? Why?

A Sample Solution

The data may be analyzed and graphed as follows.

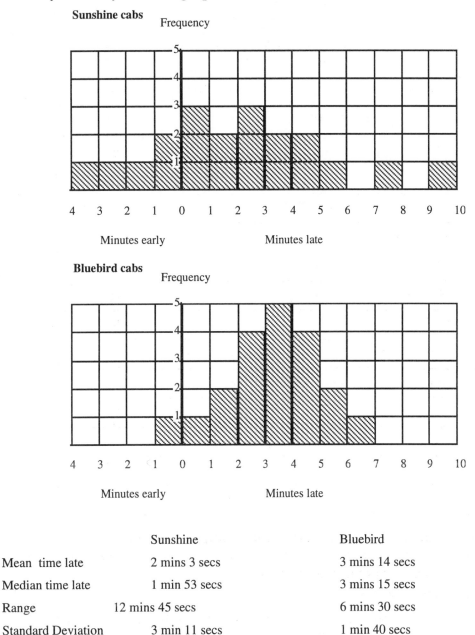

	Sunshine	Bluebird
Mean time late	2 mins 3 secs	3 mins 14 secs
Median time late	1 min 53 secs	3 mins 15 secs
Range	12 mins 45 secs	6 mins 30 secs
Standard Deviation	3 min 11 secs	1 min 40 secs

Whereas Sunshine cabs are, on average, earlier, they are less consistent in their arrival times than Bluebird cabs. It may therefore be better to book with Bluebird cabs, making sure that the cab is called about 5 minutes before it is needed.

For Formal Assessment

If you are using this task as part of a formal system of assessment, it should be presented to students with standardized instructions. You should introduce the task by reading and, where necessary, explaining the prompt.

Explain that first students have to analyze these data. This means drawing graphs or diagrams, making calculations and so on, so that comparisons may be made more easily.

It is essential that *students* are left with the choice of which statistics to use. If a student appears to be completely unable to decide, then you may offer help, but this should be recorded on the student's work when it is handed in.

For example, if you have to suggest that they find the mean time, then the word "PROMPTED" should be noted alongside the corresponding calculation.

Extensions

Some students may like to present their reasoned arguments to the whole class who may then share a discussion. Afterwards, students may like to revise their responses (using a new sheet of paper). This part may be revised and extended to form the basis of a sustained piece of work.

This section offers a characterization of student responses and provides indications of the ways in which the students were successful or unsuccessful in engaging with and completing the task. The descriptions are keyed to the Core Elements of Performance. Our global descriptions of student work range from, "The student needs significant instruction," to, " The student's work meets the essential demands of the task." Samples of student work that exemplify these descriptions of performance are included below, accompanied by commentary on central aspects of each student's response. These sample responses are *representative*; they may not mirror the global description of performance in all respects, being weaker in some and stronger in others.

The characterization of student responses for this task is based on these Core Elements of Performance:

- use appropriate measures to analyze and compare two sets of data.

- use appropriate graphs and/or diagrams to represent and analyze these data.

- present opposing reasoned cases from the same data.

- evaluate reasons and select the better case.

Descriptions of student work

The student needs significant instruction

These papers show that the student understands the prompt and attempts to organize or aggregate the data in some way.

In question 1, the student attempts to organize these data, but fails to cope with the early/late distinction or makes errors in calculating totals. An attempt to draw a graph may be made but it is of an inappropriate type. There is no realization that the mean or range are appropriate statistics.

The student makes little or no progress beyond question 1.

Student A

This response shows in the answer to question 2 that an attempt has been made to count the number of times each cab company was early. The graph shows some attempt to represent these data.

The student needs some instruction

These papers show that the student clearly understands the task and has made a superficial attempt to organize, represent and analyze these data.

In question 1, the student counts the number of times each cab is early or late, but does not aggregate magnitudes of 'lateness' by calculating averages or ranges. A tally chart or simple two column frequency graph (Showing 'Times late' and 'Times early') may be drawn.

In questions 2 and 3 reasoning based on frequencies may be given. (e.g. Sunshine cabs are early more often; Bluebird cabs are never more than 6 minutes late.) Analysis never gets deeper than this.

Student B

This response attempts to calculate the mean for both sets of data, although the student has made errors and has not differentiated between early and late times. The student is also confused by the relationship between decimal notation and times expressed in hours and minutes. Thus 3.275 is interpreted as 3 minutes 3 seconds to the nearest second.

Much of the response time is spent in producing the two bar graphs. These represent the raw data in an unaggregated form, and so are limited in use. This is done carefully and accurately, but no use is made of these data in the arguments which follow.

The response also correctly calculates the percentage of occasions on which each company was late. This is the only statistic used in the argument. No reference is made to the magnitude of these arrival times nor to their range.

The student's work needs to be revised

These papers show that the student can analyze and represent data more thoroughly, choosing appropriate measures, graphs and/or diagrams. The statistics go beyond just a superficial consideration of frequencies or proportions to include at least a consideration of averages. The graphs allow sensible comparisons to be made. The student begins to analyze and present two opposing reasoned cases and attempts to evaluate them.

In question 1, the student knows an appropriate way to aggregate these data. An analysis beyond simply counting frequencies has been attempted, but with some errors. Averages or ranges have been found, perhaps incorrectly. A suitable graph or diagram has been attempted but there may be inaccuracies.

In questions 2 and 3, a partially successful attempt has been made to compare the two companies using the statistics and the graphs drawn.

In question 4, the student has not been able to evaluate which argument is stronger.

Student C

This response shows that a serious attempt has been made to organize and aggregate these data. Calculations of the averages are incorrect, and so are some aspects of the reasoning. (For example, it says that Bluebird cabs don't have any times where they are more than 5 minutes late.

The student's work meets the essential demands of the task

These papers show that the student can confidently use appropriate measures, graphs and/or diagrams to compare two sets of data; can interpret this analysis and present two opposing reasoned cases and decide on which is the most convincing. There may be a few minor technical errors in calculation or drawing/plotting.

In question 1, the student can cope with directed times and aggregates these data sensibly. Both a representative value (e.g. the mean) and a measure of spread (e.g. the range) have been calculated, perhaps with a minor error. An appropriate representation is chosen and drawn reasonably accurately.

In questions 2 and 3, the reasoning is clear and considers at least three of: frequencies, proportions, averages, and spreads.

In question 4, an appropriate conclusion is drawn.

Student D

The response calculates a variety of statistics for each company, shows an ability to handle directed times efficiently (although the student has made an error in the calculation of the mean for Bluebird Cabs), and mentions both the mean and spread of the results in the argument.

Student A

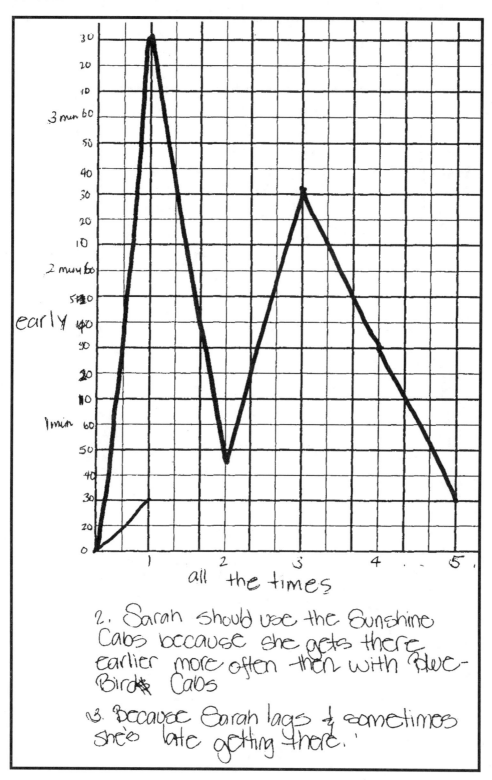

all the times

2. Sarah should use the Sunshine Cabs because she gets there earlier more often then with Blue-Bird Cabs

3. because Sarah lags & sometimes she's late getting there.

Student B

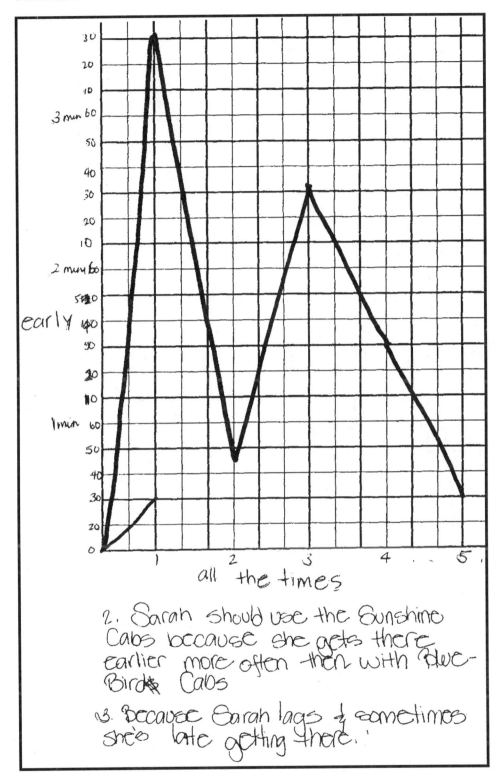

3 mun

2 mun

early

1 mun

all the times

2. Sarah should use the Sunshine Cabs because she gets there earlier more often then with Blue-Bird Cabs

3. Because Sarah lags & sometimes she's late getting there.

(time)

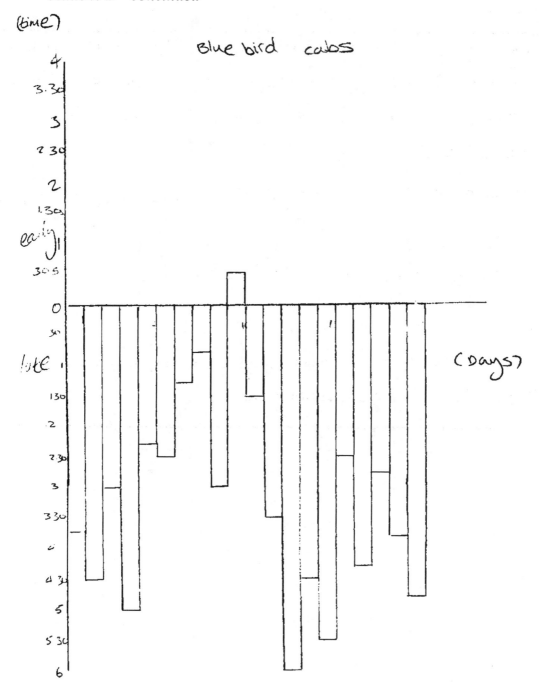

Blue bird cabs

4
3.30
3
2 30
2
1.30
early 1
30 s
0
30
late 1
1 30
2
2 30
3
3 30

4 30
5
5 30
6

(Days)

② Sunshine cabs are the better company for Sarah to use in the future because the blue bird cabs has a 95% chance of being late where as ~~Sun~~ Sunshine cabs have 75% chance of being late.

The Sunshine cabs has a 25% possibility of it coming early.

③ ___ 5% possibility of coming early

④ ~~I~~ I think the Sunshine cabs argument is convincing than the blue bird cabs argument because it has a 25% chance of coming early.

$$\frac{65m\,5s}{20} = 3 \cdot 275 \qquad \text{average for Blue bird cabs } 3\text{mins } 3\text{ secs Late}$$

$$\frac{55m\,5s}{20} = 2 \cdot 775 \text{ average for Sunshine cabs } 2\text{ mins } 8\text{secs Late}$$

Sunshine cabs		Blue bird cabs	
Early	late.	Early	late
5 days	15 days	1 day.	19 days.

Average of being late $= \dfrac{15}{20} = 0 \cdot 75 = 1$min 15secs

Sunshine cabs.

Average of being late $= \dfrac{14}{20} = 0 \cdot 95$ 1min 35sec

Blue bird cabs

<u>Sunshine cabs</u>

75% chance of being late for 1min 15 secs

25% chance of them being early.

Blue bird cabs

95% chance of being late for 1min 35 sec.

5% chance of being early.

Student C

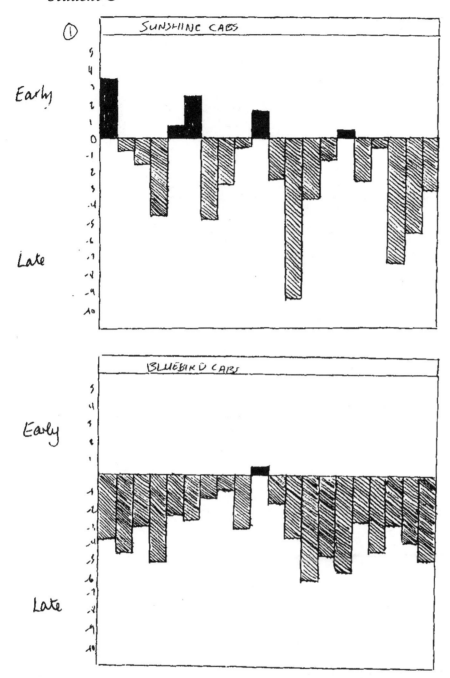

Student C – continued

Blue bird

Early	Late
30 sec	225 sec.
	270 sec.
	180 sec.
	300 sec.
	135 sec.
	150 sec.
	75 sec.
	45 sec.
	180 sec.
	90 sec.
	210 sec.
	360 sec.
	270 sec.
	330 sec.
	150 sec.
	255 sec.
	165 sec.
	225 sec.
	285 sec.

Average is 163 sec.
late overall
Late 19 times. Early 1 time.

Sunshine

Early	Late
210	45 sec.
45	90 sec.
150	270 sec.
90	285 sec.
30	165 sec.
	30 sec.
	135 sec.
	55 sec.
	210 sec.
	75 sec.
	150 sec.
	30 sec.
	435 sec.
	330 sec.
	180 sec.

Average overall
is 94 sec. late
Late 15 times. Early
5 times.

2. Well Sunsine cabs would be the best choice if she wanted to get to school at an average better time. Somtimes the cab runs very late. It has an average of 94 sec. being late.

3. Well Bluebird cabs would run at 163 sec. average being late but they don't have anny times where they were more than 5 minites late. They are hardly ever early. If you couldn't be more than 5 miturets late to school, this cab would be the correct choice.

4. I feel that sunrise cabs is the correct choice because it get's to school at an average alot sooner than the other, Bluebird cabs. Although it is somtimes later it, I feel, is the odvious correct choice.

ORDERING A CAB

① Sunshine Cabs – Early – 5/20 Late – 15/20 = Early – 25% Late – 75%
Bluebird Cabs – Early – 1/20 Late – 19/20 = Early – 5% Late – 95%

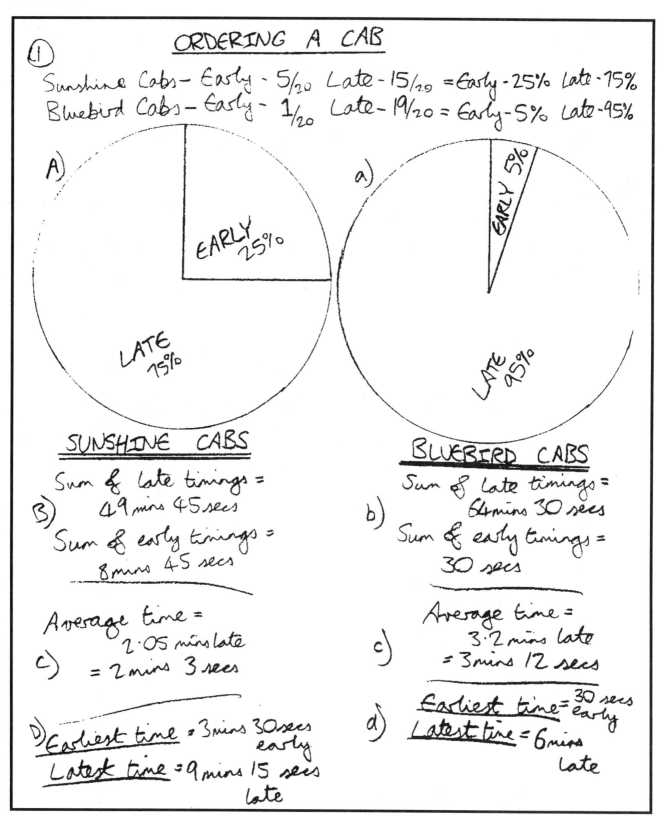

A) EARLY 25%

LATE 75%

a) EARLY 5%

LATE 95%

SUNSHINE CABS

B) Sum of late timings =
49 mins 45 secs
Sum of early timings =
8 mins 45 secs

Average time =
2·05 mins late
C) = 2 mins 3 secs

D) <u>Earliest time</u> = 3 mins 30 secs early
<u>Latest time</u> = 9 mins 15 secs late

BLUEBIRD CABS

b) Sum of late timings =
64 mins 30 secs
Sum of early timings =
30 secs

Average time =
3·2 mins late
c) = 3 mins 12 secs

d) <u>Earliest time</u> = 30 secs early
<u>Latest time</u> = 6 mins late

(2) Sunshine Cabs were early 5 times more than Bluebird Cabs - 25% of the time as opposed to only 5%. The average time of the Sunshine Cabs was 2mins 3 secs late, whereas the average time of the Bluebird Cabs was 3mins 12secs late.

(3) The Sunshine cabs are much more erratic than Bluebird cabs. The latest that a Sunshine cab arrived was 9mins 15secs, whereas the latest arrival of any Bluebird was only 6mins.

(4) I think the argument for Bluebird cabs is more convincing. If I was trying to catch a plane or something like that, I would not want my cab to be as late as 9 mins 15 secs or 7 mins 15 secs, so I would probably rather avoid a company that could turn up at those times.

Sort them

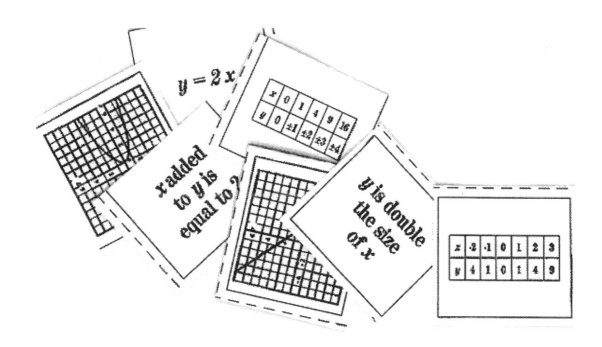

Task Description

Grade Level: High

In this task 10 functions or relations are presented. Each function or relation is expressed in four ways; a graph, a formula, a table, and in words. The representations are jumbled. The task is that of sorting the information into sets of four equivalent expressions.

> *Translate among verbal, tabular, graphical, and algebraic representations.*

Assumed Mathematical Background

Work with linear functions and quadratics is assumed.

Core Elements of Performance

- Translate among verbal, tabular, graphical, and algebraic representations of functions or relations.

Circumstances

Grouping: Students may work in pairs, but each student must turn in his or her own response to the task.

Materials: scissors, glue stick, paper, and pencil.

Estimated time: 45 minutes

Sort them

The aim of this assessment is to provide the opportunity for you to:
• sort among verbal, tabular, graphical, and algebraic representations of functions or relations.

Ten different functions or relations are given below, and each function or relation is presented in four ways:

- a graph;
- a formula;
- a table;
- in words.

Each set of four cards that is given on pages 2 and 3 is **not** grouped correctly. It is your job to sort the cards into equivalent sets.

First, cut out all of the cards.
Then, working with your partner, decide how they should be sorted.
Finally, working on your own, paste each equivalent set onto a sheet of binder paper.

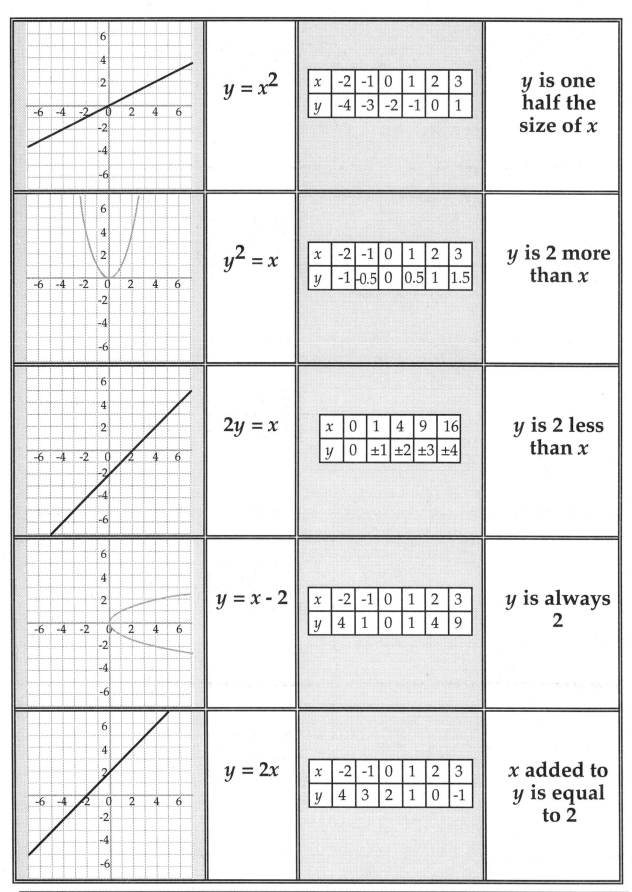

| | $y = x^2$ | | y is one half the size of x |

x	-2	-1	0	1	2	3
y	-4	-3	-2	-1	0	1

| | $y^2 = x$ | | y is 2 more than x |

x	-2	-1	0	1	2	3
y	-1	-0.5	0	0.5	1	1.5

| | $2y = x$ | | y is 2 less than x |

x	0	1	4	9	16
y	0	±1	±2	±3	±4

| | $y = x - 2$ | | y is always 2 |

x	-2	-1	0	1	2	3
y	4	1	0	1	4	9

| | $y = 2x$ | | x added to y is equal to 2 |

x	-2	-1	0	1	2	3
y	4	3	2	1	0	-1

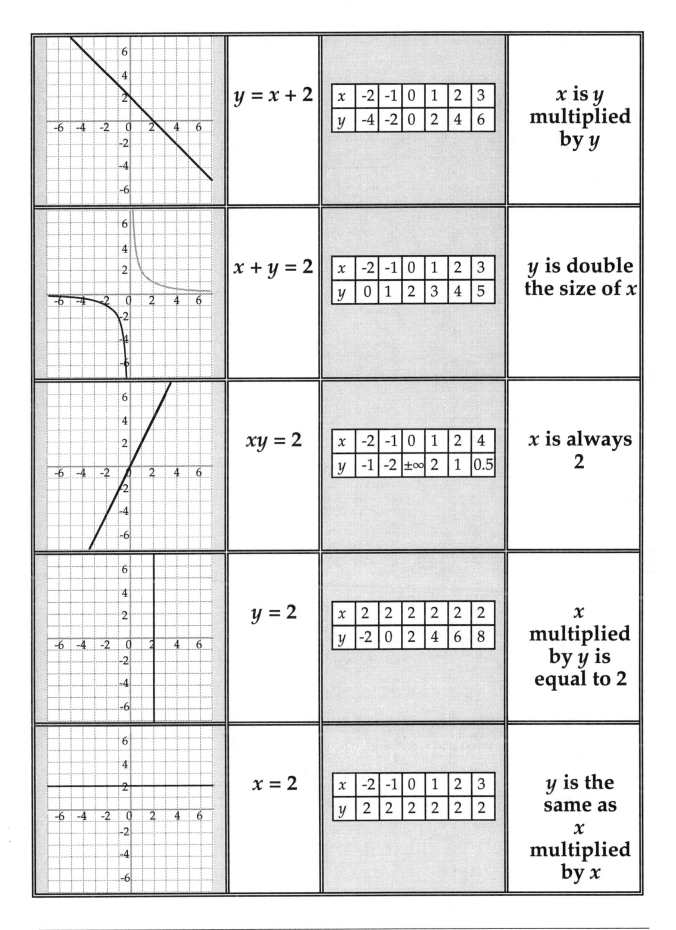

x	-2	-1	0	1	2	3
y	-4	-2	0	2	4	6

$y = x + 2$

x is y multiplied by y

x	-2	-1	0	1	2	3
y	0	1	2	3	4	5

$x + y = 2$

y is double the size of x

x	-2	-1	0	1	2	4
y	-1	-2	$\pm\infty$	2	1	0.5

$xy = 2$

x is always 2

x	2	2	2	2	2	2
y	-2	0	2	4	6	8

$y = 2$

x multiplied by y is equal to 2

x	-2	-1	0	1	2	3
y	2	2	2	2	2	2

$x = 2$

y is the same as x multiplied by x

A Sample Solution

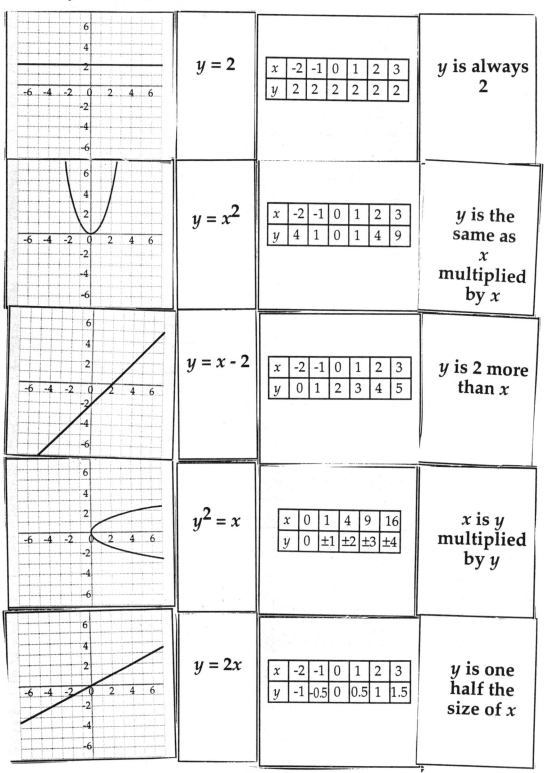

| | $y = 2$ | | | | | | | | | | | y is always 2 |

x	-2	-1	0	1	2	3
y	2	2	2	2	2	2

$y = x^2$ — y is the same as x multiplied by x

x	-2	-1	0	1	2	3
y	4	1	0	1	4	9

$y = x - 2$ — y is 2 more than x

x	-2	-1	0	1	2	3
y	0	1	2	3	4	5

$y^2 = x$ — x is y multiplied by y

x	0	1	4	9	16
y	0	±1	±2	±3	±4

$y = 2x$ — y is one half the size of x

x	-2	-1	0	1	2	3
y	-1	-0.5	0	0.5	1	1.5

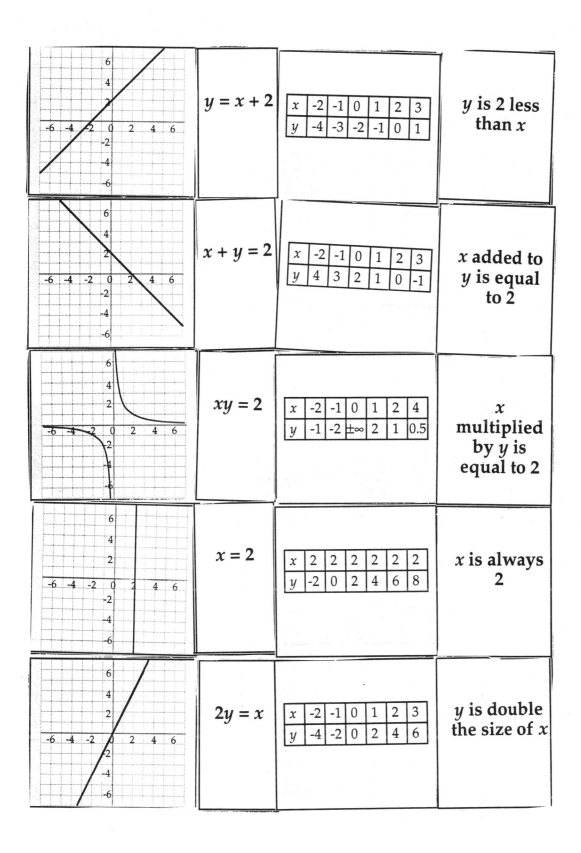

| $y = x + 2$ | x | -2 | -1 | 0 | 1 | 2 | 3 | y is 2 less than x |
| | y | -4 | -3 | -2 | -1 | 0 | 1 | |

| $x + y = 2$ | x | -2 | -1 | 0 | 1 | 2 | 3 | x added to y is equal to 2 |
| | y | 4 | 3 | 2 | 1 | 0 | -1 | |

| $xy = 2$ | x | -2 | -1 | 0 | 1 | 2 | 4 | x multiplied by y is equal to 2 |
| | y | -1 | -2 | $\pm\infty$ | 2 | 1 | 0.5 | |

| $x = 2$ | x | 2 | 2 | 2 | 2 | 2 | 2 | x is always 2 |
| | y | -2 | 0 | 2 | 4 | 6 | 8 | |

| $2y = x$ | x | -2 | -1 | 0 | 1 | 2 | 3 | y is double the size of x |
| | y | -4 | -2 | 0 | 2 | 4 | 6 | |

For Formal Assessment

- Organize the class into groups of two.
- Give each student a copy of the task.

Here is a suggested introduction to the task.

Read through the task with the whole class to help ensure that each member understands the problem. Draw students' attention to the first set of four cards. Ask students to look at the first graph, then ask if this can this be expressed by the formula, .

Hopefully, the answer will be no. Then consider the other two cards in the same way. With the class, check to see if the table represents the graph or the formula. Do the same for the verbal statement. It will be helpful if the class realizes that the verbal statement matches the graph but no other card in the first set. Tell students that it is their job to examine all cards in this ways, and find 10 sets of matching cards. The ten sets are to be pasted onto binder paper. Once the task is explained, give out the scissors to cut the cards.

Allocate three quarters of the time available to pair consultation. In the remaining time students should work individually to present their own organized sets. At this stage students will require glue. Remind students that they might need to change their minds about what goes where and they must not paste in their solutions too quickly.

Extensions

If students finish the task early, then ask them to make up six (the number can vary according to the time available) similar sets of equivalent expressions. They must follow these constraints:

- two sets must be easy.
- two sets must be of middling difficulty.
- two sets must be extremely hard.

Each set must be labeled with its appropriate difficulty level.

This section offers a characterization of student responses and provides indications of the ways in which the students were successful or unsuccessful in engaging with and completing the task. The descriptions are keyed to the Core Elements of Performance. Our global descriptions of student work range from, "The student needs significant instruction," to, " The student's work meets the essential demands of the task." Samples of student work that exemplify these descriptions of performance are included below, accompanied by commentary on central aspects of each student's response. These sample responses are *representative*; they may not mirror the global description of performance in all respects, being weaker in some and stronger in others.

The characterization of student responses for this task is based on these Core Elements of Performance:

- translate among verbal, tabular, graphical, and algebraic representations of functions or relations.

Descriptions of student work

The student needs significant instruction

These papers show, at most, evidence of clear understanding that the student has read and understood the task.

Typically the student matches at least two representations for a few of the cases. The matches given are not always correct.

Student A

The response shows some sorting.

The student needs some instruction

These papers provide evidence of that the student inconsistently sorts the representations.

Student B

This response shows some correctly sorted cases. The graphs among other representations are not sorted correctly.

The student's work needs to be revised

Aspects of the task are not complete.

Student C

This response shows representations that are sorted correctly, but the response is not complete.

The student's work meets the essential demands of the task

All or almost all aspects of the task are present and complete.

Typically there are no errors.

Student D

This response shows a complete set of correctly sorted representations.

Student A

1. $y = x + 2$	2. y is 2 more than x	3.	4.
5. $x = 2$	6. x is always 2	7.	8.
9. $y = x^2$	10. y is one half the size of x	11.	12.
13. $y = 2x$	14. y is the same as $x \times x$	15.	16.
17.	18.	19.	20.

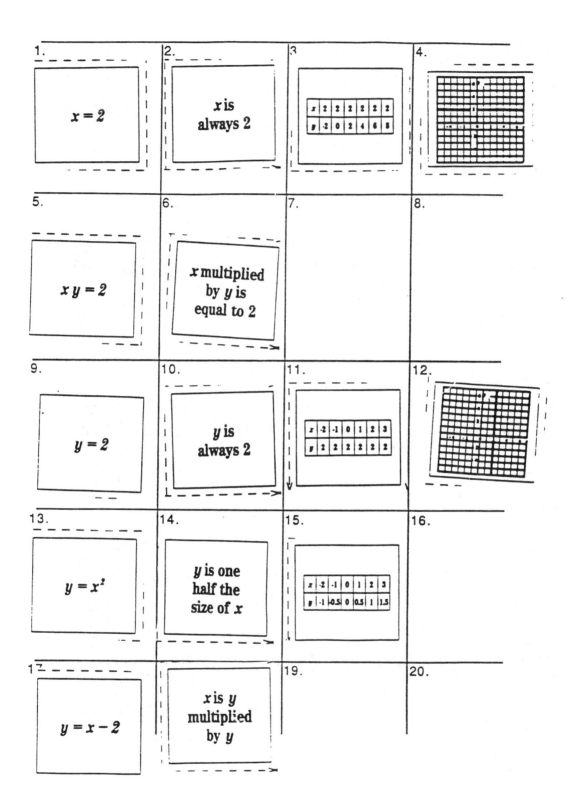

1. $x = 2$

2. *x* is always 2

3.

x	2	2	2	2	2
y	-2	0	2	4	6	8

4.

5. $x\,y = 2$

6. *x* multiplied by *y* is equal to 2

7.

8.

9. $y = 2$

10. *y* is always 2

11.

x	-2	-1	0	1	2	3
y	2	2	2	2	2	2

12.

13. $y = x^2$

14. *y* is one half the size of *x*

15.

x	-2	-1	0	1	2	3
y	-1	-0.5	0	0.5	1	1.5

16.

17. $y = x - 2$

18.

19. *x* is *y* multiplied by *y*

20.

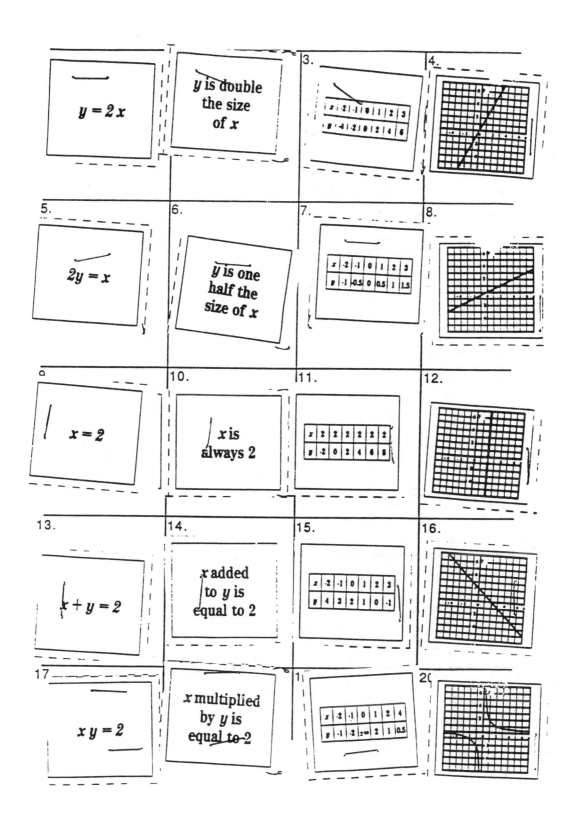

1. $y = 2x$

2. y is double the size of x

3.

x	-2	-1	0	1	2	3
y	-4	-2	0	2	4	6

4.

5. $2y = x$

6. y is one half the size of x

7.

x	-2	-1	0	1	2	3
y	-1	-0.5	0	0.5	1	1.5

8.

9. $x = 2$

10. x is always 2

11.

x	2	2	2	2	2	2
y	-2	0	2	4	6	8

12.

13. $x + y = 2$

14. x added to y is equal to 2

15.

x	-2	-1	0	1	2	3
y	4	3	2	1	0	-1

16.

17. $xy = 2$

18. x multiplied by y is equal to 2

19.

x	-2	-1	0	1	2	4
y	-1	-2	2	2	1	0.5

20.

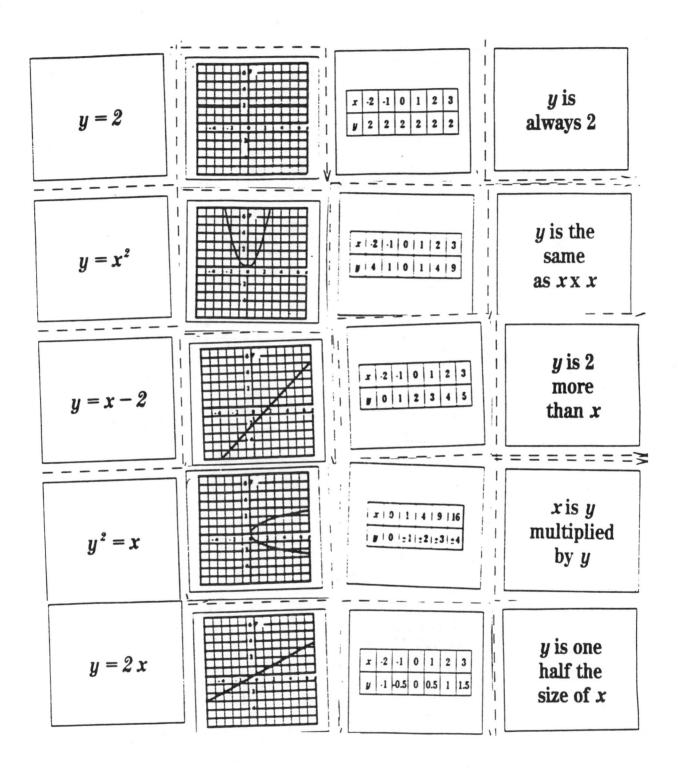

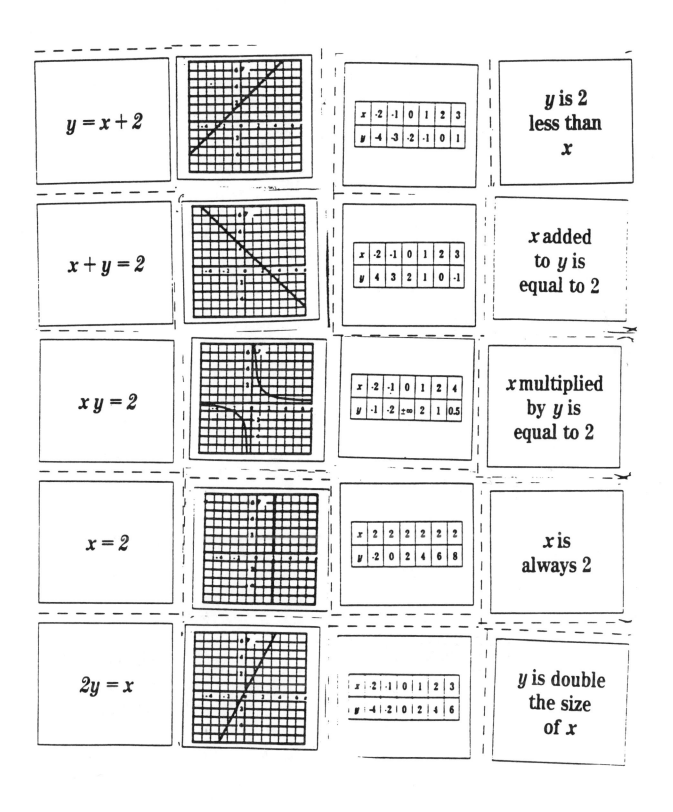

x	-2	-1	0	1	2	3
y	-4	-3	-2	-1	0	1

$y = x + 2$

y is 2 less than x

x	-2	-1	0	1	2	3
y	4	3	2	1	0	-1

$x + y = 2$

x added to y is equal to 2

x	-2	-1	0	1	2	4
y	-1	-2	$\pm\infty$	2	1	0.5

$xy = 2$

x multiplied by y is equal to 2

x	2	2	2	2	2	2
y	-2	0	2	4	6	8

$x = 2$

x is always 2

x	-2	-1	0	1	2	3
y	-4	-2	0	2	4	6

$2y = x$

y is double the size of x

Task Description

Grade Level: High

In this task students are asked to organize a number of jobs according to precedence constraints, while at the same time trying to optimize the total time needed to complete the house.

Probably the best way of proceeding is to cut out the job cards from the provided sheet and physically organize them on the table top. This should be suggested to students who are in difficulty. If you do help them in this way, then please record this fact at the bottom of their work.

> *Interpret a real life problem.*
>
> *Organize information.*
>
> *Design and use charts or diagrams.*
>
> *Solve an optimization problem.*

Assumed Mathematical Background

It is assumed that students have some experience of solving problems which require them to organize information, use charts or diagrams, and communicate their solution.

Core Elements of Performance

- Interpret a problem set in a realistic context.
- Organize information subject to constraints.
- Design and use appropriate charts or diagrams.
- Solve an optimization problem.

Circumstances

Grouping: Students work individually or in pairs. Pair work should encourage discussion. Each member of a pair, however, must produce his or her own written solution.

Materials: Each pair of students will need a pair of scissors.

Estimated time: 45 minutes

House in a hurry

The aim of this assessment is to provide the opportunity for you to:
- *interpret a real life problem.*
- *organize information.*
- *design and use charts or diagrams.*
- *solve a problem.*

You work for a construction company and receive this memo:

Memo   Rapido Builders Inc.

From: Phil Hernandez
To: You
Re: We need this contract!
Date: Friday Feb. 26th

We have the chance to get a big contract to build a house on the corner of Alameda Avenue. The customers have already chosen the plans. They are in a hurry and will give this contract to the construction company that can complete the job in the **SHORTEST** amount of time. I think we stand a good chance, so let's go for it!

I have attached a list of the jobs to be done and the requirements for each job.

Please prepare a schedule which clearly shows how we should organize the work.

Use some kind of diagram or chart to show when each job will be started and finished, and let me know the earliest possible date when we can finish the house.

Remember:

- We must begin on Monday morning, 1st March. (Get some concrete for the foundations this weekend.)

- No work will be carried out on weekends. It is too expensive to pay overtime.

- We have a big enough work force to do more than one job at the same time - so use it!

- Make a clear record of your reasoning. I want to check it!

Write your reply to the memo.

	March				
Sun		7	14	21	28
Mon	1	8	15	22	29
Tues	2	9	16	23	30
Wed	3	10	17	24	31
Thur	4	11	18	25	
Fri	5	12	19	26	
Sat	6	13	20	27	

JOB A
Plastering the walls

This takes: 2 working days
Before starting:
You must put in the plumbing and wiring (JOB I) and erect the roof (JOB B).

JOB B
Erecting the roof

This takes: 6 working days

Before starting:
You must build the walls (JOB E)

JOB C
Pouring the concrete to make the foundations

This takes: 2 working days

JOB D
Landscaping the surroundings

This takes: 8 working days
You can only start this when the messy building work in JOB B is finished.

JOB E
Building the walls and putting in the windows and doors

This takes: 10 working days
Before starting:
You must do JOB C and JOB G.

JOB F
Painting

This takes: 3 working days
Before starting:
You must install the cupboards and other fitted furniture (JOB H).

JOB G
Ordering and waiting for timber, bricks, windows and doors to be delivered

This takes: 7 working days

JOB H
Installing cupboards and other fitted furniture

This takes: 2 working days
Before starting:
You must order and wait for the furniture (JOB J) and plaster the walls (JOB A).

JOB I
Putting in the plumbing and wiring

This takes: 8 working days
Before starting:
You must build the walls (JOB E)

JOB J
Ordering and waiting for cupboards and other fitted furniture to be delivered

This takes: 15 working days

A Sample Solution

The required order of jobs is shown in the diagram below.

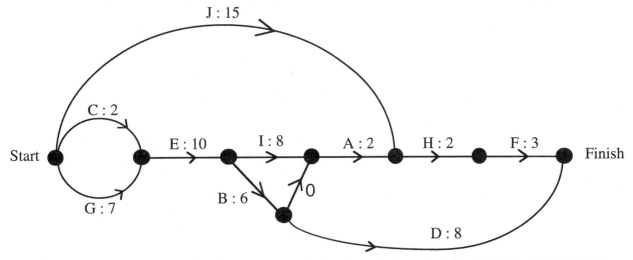

The path which takes the longest time, working from left to right is G, E, I, A, H, F. This shows that the job must take at least 32 working days (= 7 + 10 + 8 + 2 + 2 + 3). As the job is begun on Monday, March 1st, it can be completed at the end of Tuesday, April 13th. The following time chart shows one of several possible correct solutions.

Mon 1	G	J	C	Tues 16	E	J	Wed 31	I	B
Tues 2	G	J	C	Wed 17	E	J	Thur 1	I	D
Wed 3	G	J		Thur 18	E	J	Fri 2	I	D
Thur 4	G	J		Fri 19	E	J	Sat 3		
Fri 5	G	J		Sat 20			Sun 4		
Sat 6				Sun 21			Mon 5	A	D
Sun 7				Mon 22	E		Tues 6	A	D
Mon 8	G	J		Tues 23	E		Wed 7	H	D
Tues 9	G	J		Wed 24	I	B	Thur 8	H	D
Wed 10	E	J		Thur 25	I	B	Fri 9	F	D
Thur 11	E	J		Fri 26	I	B	Sat 10		
Fri 12	E	J		Sat 27			Sun 11		
Sat 13				Sun 28			Mon 12	F	D
Sun 14				Mon 29	I	B	Tues 13	F	
Mon 15	E	J		Tues 30	I	B	Wed 14		

For Formal Assessment

There are standard 'critical path analysis' algorithms for solving problems such as this, but these are normally taught at a higher level than Grade 10. Here we are not assessing the student's ability to deploy such an algorithm, rather we are trying to assess general problem solving skills. In particular, the task is designed to assess how far a student is able to:

- organize information, subject to constraints.

- design and use appropriate charts or diagrams.

- communicate a clear, reasoned, solution to an optimization problem.

This section offers a characterization of student responses and provides indications of the ways in which the students were successful or unsuccessful in engaging with and completing the task. The descriptions are keyed to the Core Elements of Performance. Our global descriptions of student work range from, "The student needs significant instruction," to, "The student's work meets the essential demands of the task." Samples of student work that exemplify these descriptions of performance are included below, accompanied by commentary on central aspects of each student's response. These sample responses are *representative*; they may not mirror the global description of performance in all respects, being weaker in some and stronger in others.

The characterization of student responses for this task is based on these Core Elements of Performance:

- interpret a problem set in a realistic context.
- organize information subject to constraints.
- design and use appropriate charts or diagrams.
- solve an optimization problem.

Descriptions of student work

The student needs significant instruction

These papers show, at most, evidence of clear understanding of the fact that the ten jobs need to be organized in a time sequence.

Typically, the jobs are organized in an (almost) acceptable order, but no attempt is made to look for jobs which can be worked on at the same time.

Student A

Student A has managed to organize the jobs into a satisfactory order, but has not considered the fact that several jobs may be done in parallel.

The student needs some instruction

These papers provide evidence of understanding that the jobs need to be organized in a time sequence and that some of the jobs can be worked on at the same time.

Typically, the jobs are organized in an acceptable order and some attempt is made to consider which jobs can be worked on at the same time. There may be no attempt to relate the work to the calendar.

Student B

Student B has tried to group the jobs that may be done in parallel, then order each group, showing the starting times of each job (in days) after the beginning of the project. There are, however, a number of errors. For example, the assumption is made that job E may begin on day 3, whereas it should wait until job G is completed. Also, it is assumed that jobs H and F may be done in parallel, when the cards explicitly forbid this. The assumption has also been made, incorrectly, that job D can only be started after job I is completed, and that jobs H and F can only be started after job D is finished. This student has not tried to relate the work to the calendar.

The student's work needs to be revised

These papers provide evidence of understanding that the jobs need to be organized in a time sequence and that some of the jobs can be worked on at the same time. The jobs are allocated to working days on the calendar provided.

Typically, responses may not be completely correct in organizing the job sequence and allocating jobs to dates on the calendar.

Student C

Student C has organized the jobs along a time sequence correctly, except for job A, which should precede job H. When allocating jobs to dates on the calendar, this student has allowed 7 days for job G instead of 7 *working* days. Consequently, job E should not begin until Wednesday 10. This error results in other jobs needing to move on by 2 days.

The student's work meets the essential demands of the task

These papers provide evidence of understanding that the jobs need to be organized in a time sequence and that some of the jobs can be worked on at the same time. The jobs are allocated to working days on the calendar provided.

Typically, almost all of the requirements of the tasks are met with only minor errors.

Student D

This is a high level response.
Although Job F has been ignored, Student D has shown a considerable degree of skill in organizing the information and presenting it so clearly.

Student A

Building a house.

Job G = ordering and waiting for the windows and doors to be delivered. This takes 7 days.

Job C = Pouring concrete to make foundations This takes two days.

Job E = Building the walls, This takes 10 days

Job I = Putting in the plumbing, This takes 8 days

Job B = Erecting the roof, This takes 6 days.

Job J = Ordering and waiting for the cupboards and furniture to be delivered, This takes 15 days.

Job D = Landscaping the surroundings, This takes 8 days.

Job A = Plastering the walls, This takes 2 days

Job H = Installing cupboards and furniture this takes 2 days.

Job F = painting inside and outside.
63 days = 9 week + 18 days for the weekends.

The total time is 11 ½ weeks. to build the house

The date when I will have finished building this house would be the 2nd may!

To start with I found it a little bit difficult but then once I clicked how to do it, it was easy!

1) Job J,G,C, you can order the cupboards, furniture, and windows and doors, and someone else be pouring the concrete. 2 days to pour the concrete and do other stuff while you wait

$\underline{1}$st day

2) Job E, building the walls and putting in the windows and doors. 10 days

3rd day

3) Job B,I erect the roof and put in the plumbing and wiring. 8 days

$\underline{13}$th days

4) Job D,A landscaping the surroundings and someone else plastering walls. 8 days

21st day

5) Job H,F Installing cupboards and furniture and some other painting outside until the stuff is installed and then do the inside 3 days

29 day

32 days

Mon 1st	Tues 2nd	Wed 3rd	Thurs 4th	Fri 5th	Sat 6th	Sun 7th
C J G	C J G	J G	J G	J G	J G	J G
Mon 8th	**Tues 9th**	**Wed 10th**	**Thurs 11th**	**Fri 12th**	**Sat 13th**	**Sun 14th**
J E	J E	J E	J E	J E	J	J
Mon 15th	**Tues 16th**	**Wed 17th**	**Thurs 18th**	**Fri 19th**	**Sat 20th**	**Sun 21st**
J E	E	E	E	E		
Mon 22nd	**Tues 23rd**	**Wed 24th**	**Thurs 25th**	**Fri 26th**	**Sat 27th**	**Sun 28th**
B I	B I	B I	B I	B I		
Mon 29th	**Tues 30th**	**Wed 31st**	**Thurs 1st**	**Fri 2nd**	**Sat 3rd**	**Sun 4th**
B I	I	I	H D	H D		
Mon 5th	**Tues 6th**	**Wed 7th**	**Thurs 8th**	**Fri 9th**	**Sat 10th**	**Sun 11th**
F A D	F A D	F D	D	D		
Mon 12th	**Tues 13th**	**Wed 14th**	**Thurs 15th**	**Fri 16th**	**Sat 17th**	**Sun 18th**
D	FINISH					

1st = Pour Foundations
   Order Furniture
   Order Windows
8th = Build Walls
22th = Erect Roof
   Put in plumbing
1st = Landscape surroundings
   Installing Furniture
5th = Painting (Inside and Outside)
   Plastering Walls

Earliest Possible Finishing Date:
Monday 12th April
43 days

Student D

March

Sun	Mon	Tues	Wed	Thur	Fri	Sat
	1 C G J	2 C G J	3 G J	4 G J	5 G J	6
7	8 G J	9 G J	10 E J	11 E J	12 E J	13
14	15 E J	16 E J	17 E J	18 E J	19 E J	20
21 non work days	22 E	23 E	24 B I	25 B I	26 B I	27 non work days
28	29 B I	30 B I	31 B I	April 1 D I	2 D I	3
4	5 D A	6 D A	7 D H	8 D H	9 D	10
11	12 D finish	13	14	15	16	17

Memo

If we start on March 1st and work every working day the house should be finished by April 12. This is taking advantage of every working day.

Checking an odometer

Task Description

Grade Level: Secondary

A situation is presented involving a circular track for bicycles. Every lap of the track is exactly 0.4 kilometers long.

But the bicycle being used on the track has an odometer that is inaccurate by a consistent percent error. Students are asked to correlate the readings on the odometer with actual distances traveled.

> *Relate instrument readings to real values when there is a consistent percent error in the readings.*
>
> *Use proportional reasoning.*

Assumed Mathematical Background

Students should have had some experience using proportional reasoning, and figuring percentages, such as percent error.

Core Elements of Performance

The task provides students with the opportunity to:
- use proportional reasoning to relate instrument readings to real values when there is a consistent percent error in the readings.
- construct a table and a graph that show the relationship between true values and instrument readings.
- construct a rule or formula that converts instrument readings to true values.
- construct another rule or formula that converts true values to instrument readings.
- characterize the instrument in terms of its "percent error".

Circumstances

Grouping: Students work individually.

Materials: paper, pencil, calculator, ruler

Estimated time: 45 minutes

Task 6050

Checking an odometer

The aim of this assessment is to provide the opportunity for you to:

- *use proportional reasoning to relate odometer readings to real distances when there is a consistent percent error in the odometer readings.*

- *characterize the instrument in terms of its "percent error".*

An odometer is a device that measures how far a bicycle (or a car) travels.
Sometimes an odometer is not adjusted accurately.
It will then give readings which are consistently too high or too low.

Paul does an experiment to check his bicycle odometer.
He cycles 10 laps around a race track.
One lap of the track is exactly 0.4 kilometers long.

When he starts his odometer looks like this:

After 10 laps his odometer looks like this:

1. Paul continues to cycle round the track, doing a total of 60 laps.
    Copy and complete the table below. (Use a calculator.)

Number of laps	0	10	20	30	40	50	60
Distance Paul *really* travels (km)	0	4					
Distance odometer *says* Paul travels (km)	0	3.40					

2. Draw a graph to show how the distance shown by the odometer is related to the real distance traveled.
    Label your axes as shown below. Is the graph a straight line?

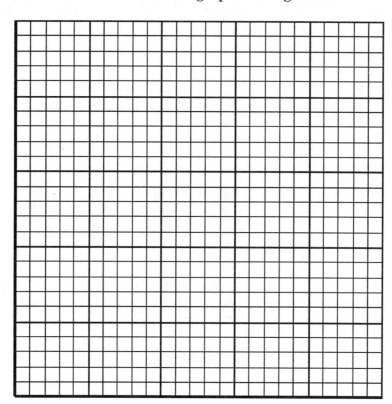

Distance Paul has *really* traveled

3. (a) When Paul *really* travels 1 km, how far does his odometer *say* he has traveled?
    (b) When his odometer *says* he has traveled 1 km, how far has he *really* traveled?

4. How far has Paul *really* traveled, when the odometer looks like this? Describe your method clearly.

5. Find a rule or formula that Paul can use to change his incorrect odometer readings into real distances he has gone from the start of his ride. ("Real" means "accurate" here.)
Show how your formula works to answer question 4.

6. Paul wants to see how long it takes to go 25 km. If he starts when his odometer reads 1945.6, what will his odometer read when he has really gone exactly 25 km?

7. Find a formula Paul can use to change real distances he has gone into odometer readings. Show how your formula works to answer question 6.

8. Is this statement correct?

| Paul's odometer has a 10% error |

If it is, then explain how you know the error is 10%.
If it is not, then what should the correct statement be?

A Sample Solution

1. Every 10 laps the real distance increases 4.0 km and the odometer distance increases 3.4 km.

Number of laps	0	10	20	30	40	50	60
Distance Paul *really* travels (km)	0	4	8	12	16	20	24
Distance odometer *says* Paul travels (km)	0	3.40	6.80	10.20	13.60	17.00	20.40

2. The 7 data points from the table have been graphed. They all fall a straight line. (This is as it should be, since odometer distances are *proportional* to real distances.)
   For reference, a dotted line is drawn that would indicate a fully accurate odometer.

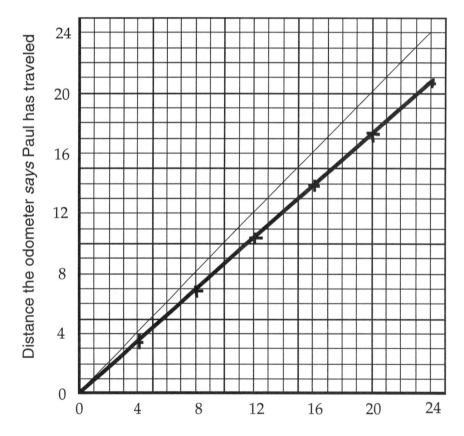

Distance Paul has *really* traveled

3. A way of thinking about this is to realize that the odometer distance and the real distance are always in the same ratio:
$$\frac{\text{odometer distance}}{\text{real distance}} = \frac{3.4}{4} = 0.85.$$

(3a) From the above, a general rule is:
(odometer distance) = (0.85) (real distance).
So when Paul really travels 1 km, his odometer says he has traveled
(0.85) (1 km) = 0.85 km.

(3b) From the above, a general rule is:
$$(\text{real distance}) = \frac{\text{odometer distance}}{0.85}$$
Alternatively:
(real distance) ≈ (1.176) (odometer distance)
So when Paul's odometer says he has traveled 1 km, he has really traveled about:
$$\frac{1 \text{ km}}{0.85} \approx 1.176 \text{ km}.$$

4. When the odometer reads 1960.00, the odometer says he traveled:
1960.00 - 1945.60 = 14.40 km.
So he has really traveled:
$$\frac{14.40}{0.85} \approx 16.94 \text{ km}.$$
(See question 3b)
(Some students may interpret the question as asking for the total distance traveled from the time the odometer read 0, and answer $\frac{1960}{0.85} \approx 2306$ km.)

5. See the solution to #3 and #4.
The general rule is:
$$\text{real distance traveled} = \frac{\text{odometer reading - 1945.60}}{0.85}.$$

6. In 25 real kilometers the odometer will increase by (25) (0.85) = 21.25 km. (See question 3a.) So the odometer reading would be 1945.6 + 21.25 = 1966.85.

7. See the solution to #3 and #4.
The general rule is:
odometer reading = 1945.60 + (0.85) (real distance traveled).

8. The percent error is **not** 10%.
The total error in a real distance of 4 km is 0.6 km (= 4.0 - 3.4).
The percent error is then $100 \left(\frac{0.6}{4}\right) = 15\%$.

For Formal Assessment

Some students may not know what an odometer is. If so, there may need to be a short class discussion on odometers. It may be useful to contrast them with speedometers. Also, students need to see that when an odometer is inaccurate, it is usually not just "wrong" in a random way, but is "off" in a consistent way. If so, correct distances can be deduced from its readings.

In this task, students will see that the odometer goes up only 0.85 for every real 1.00 kilometer traveled. From this some will think that they need to **add** 0.15 to an odometer distance to get a real distance. Actually they need to **multiply** a real distance by 0.85 to get an odometer distance. This task thus addresses the question "do you add or multiply?"

This task can be confusing since students have to keep track of three kinds of quantities:

    -*odometer* **readings**   (1945.60, etc.),

    -*odometer* **distances** (these are obtained by subtracting one odometer reading
                            from another),

    -**real** *distances*   (these are related to the odometer distances by a consistent
                            factor).

Two important ideas are involved here.

(1)   One is the idea that we can associate an "error factor" **E** with the odometer:

$$E \; = \; \frac{\text{odometer distance}}{\text{true distance}} \; = \; \frac{3.4}{4} \; = \; 0.85$$

This enables us to convert "true" distances to "odometer" distances:

    (A)   odometer distance = (0.85) (true distance).

It also enables us to convert "odometer" distances to "true" distances:

    (B)   true distance = $\dfrac{\text{odometer distance}}{0.85} \approx (1.176)$ (odometer distance).

The two parts of question 3 get at this idea directly.

(2)   The other basic idea is the way the concepts in (1) relate to actual readings on the odometer; for example, the reading 1945.60 at the start and the reading 1949.00 after 10 laps. It is not these readings themselves but their **difference** 1949.00 - 1945.60 = 3.40 that is important in figuring out the odometer error.

     Suppose you want to know what the odometer will read after you have gone some fixed real distance. You need to use the concepts of (1) to find the *odometer* distance for that real distance (by multiplying by 0.85). But then you also need to **add** this odometer distance to the starting reading 1945.60. Question 6 gets at this idea.

Extensions

Checking an odometer can be extended by adding this final question:

An odometer measures how far a bicycle travels by counting the number of times the wheel turns around. It then multiplies this number by the circumference of the wheel. To do this right the odometer has to be "set" for the right wheel circumference. If it is set for the wrong circumference, it's readings are consistently too high or too low.

(a) Before Paul's experiment he had estimated that his wheel circumference was 210 cm.
Then he had "set" his odometer for this circumference.

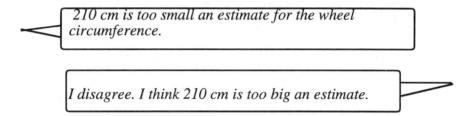

210 cm is too small an estimate for the wheel circumference.

I disagree. I think 210 cm is too big an estimate.

Which view do you agree with? Give your reasons.

(b) Use the results of his experiment to find a more accurate estimate for the circumference.

Possible responses to the extension:

(a) When the bicycle goes 4 km, the odometer says the distance is only 3.4 km. So to be accurate, the odometer has to assign each turn of the wheel a greater distance. This assignment is done when the wheel circumference is "set" on the odometer. So this setting should be greater than 210 cm.

(b) A more accurate setting would be $\dfrac{210}{0.85} \approx 247$ cm.

This section offers a characterization of student responses and provides indications of the ways in which the students were successful or unsuccessful in engaging with and completing the task. The descriptions are keyed to the Core Elements of Performance. Our global descriptions of student work range from, "The student needs significant instruction," to, "The student's work meets the essential demands of the task." Samples of student work that exemplify these descriptions of performance are included below, accompanied by commentary on central aspects of each student's response. These sample responses are *representative*; they may not mirror the global description of performance in all respects, being weaker in some and stronger in others.

The characterization of student responses for this task is based on these Core Elements of Performance:

- use proportional reasoning to relate instrument readings to real values when there is a consistent percent error in the readings.

- construct a table and a graph that show the relationship between true values and instrument readings.

- construct a rule or formula that converts instrument readings to true values.

- construct another rule or formula that converts true values to instrument readings.

- characterize the instrument in terms of its "percent error".

Descriptions of student work

The student needs significant instruction

These responses show some evidence of understanding of the context of the problem. For example, the table in question 1 may have been correctly filled in (or nearly so).

Student A

The student copies and completes the table. The student does not answer the rest of the questions.

The student needs some instruction

These responses show correct answers to some of the specific questions, but does not go on to produce any correct general rules.

Student B

The student completes the table correctly, and answers question 3 correctly, but does not give any of the general rules asked for. In addition, the percentage error given in question 8 is incorrect.

The student's work needs to be revised

These responses show use of proportional reasoning, but there is some flaw in the working out of the details. There is a rule for converting true distances to odometer distances and odometer distances to true distances, but they may not be fully correct.

Student C

The student has answered questions 1 and 3 correctly, but in answering question 2 and 4 to 6, the student has reversed odometer distances and real distances. In other words, the student has used proportional reasoning in the analysis, but has reversed the two quantities. It is reasonable to infer that if this were pointed out, the student would be able to produce a correct response.

The student's work meets the essential demands of the task

These responses show a correct proportional reasoning argument, noting that the ratio of odometer distances to real distances is always 0.85. The response has a rule for converting true distances to odometer distances, and odometer distances to true distances. In these rules, multiplication, division, subtraction, and addition are used correctly.

Student D

The student has answered questions 1 to 8 correctly. Notice that in answering #4, the student apparently has interpreted the question as asking the distance from an odometer reading of 0, rather than from a reading of 1945.6, but given that interpretation, has answered correctly. Also, question 8 has a correct answer, but no indication of how it was derived.

Student A

Assesment questions

a, 3,40 Kim

b, .4 Kim

c, too low

D, 1947,3

1. Number of laps	0	10	20	30	40	50	60
Distance Paul really travels (km)	0	<1	8	12	16	20	24
Distance odometer says Paul travels (km)	0	3,40	6,80	10,20	1360	17,00	20,40

Assessment questions

In answering these questions, remember that Paul's odometer gives readings that are consistently too low.

1. Paul continues to cycle round the track, doing a total of 60 laps.
   Copy and complete the table below. (Use a calculator.)

Number of laps	0	10	20	30	40	50	60
Distance Paul *really* travels (km)	0	4	8	12	16	.20	29
Distance odometer *says* Paul travels (km)	0	3.40	6.8	10.2	13.6	17	20.4

2. Draw a graph to show how the distance shown by the odometer is related to the real distance traveled.
   Label your axes as shown below. Is the graph a straight line?

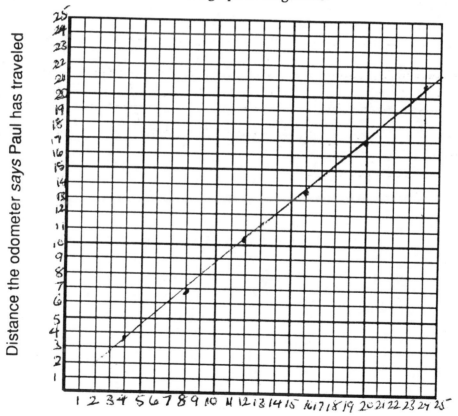

Distance the odometer *says* Paul has traveled

Distance Paul has *really* traveled

$$\frac{4}{3.4} = \frac{1}{x} \qquad x = .85 \qquad \frac{4}{3.4} = \frac{x}{1}$$

3. $a = .85$ Km
   $b = 1.18$ Km

4. $\dfrac{\underline{}}{1960} = \underline{}$

5.

6. 25 Km × .4 = 10   1945.6 | 1955.6 |
                       + 10.0

7. # of Km × .4 = | answer |

8. No, it is a 4% error.

9.

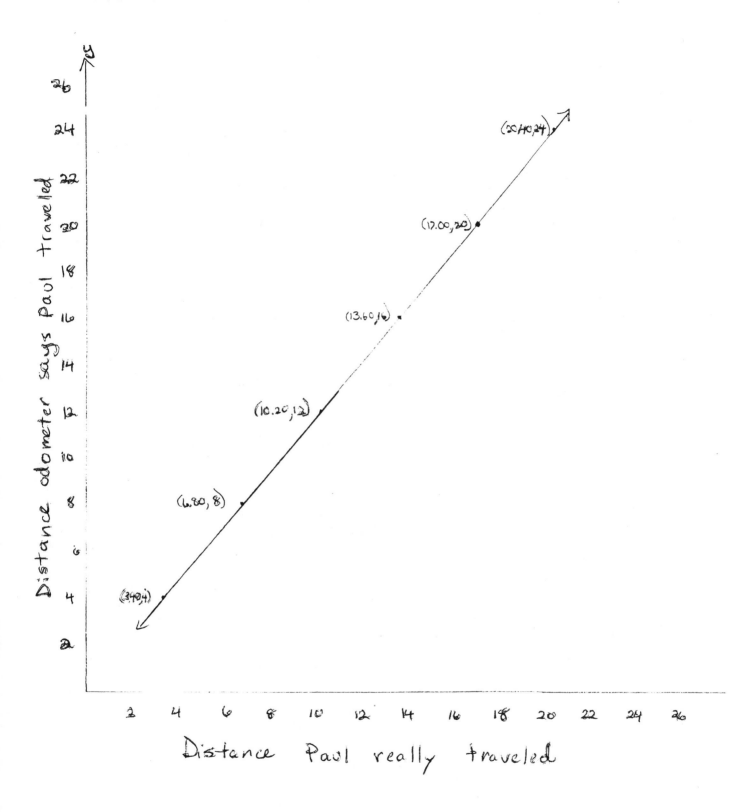

1) # of laps	0	10	20	30	40	50	60
Distance really traveled	0	4	8	12	16	20	24
Distance odometer says	0	3.40	6.80	10.20	13.60	17.00	20.40

2) see graph

3a) When Paul travels 1 Km the odometer says he has traveled 0.85 Km

b) when the odometer says Paul traveled 1 Km he has really traveled 1.18 Km

4)
$$1960.00$$
$$-1945.60$$
$$14.40$$

14.40 ÷ 1.18 = 12.20 Km
Paul has traveled 12.20 Km

To find the distance traveled you subtract the original distance from 1960.00 to get the difference, then you take this difference and divide it by 1.18 (the difference in accuracy) and you get the distance he has really traveled

5) He should subtract the original reading (1945.60) from the reading he has and divides it by 1.18 to get the amount he has really traveled
x= current reading   x - 1945.60 = y , then
y= distance odometer says   y ÷ 1.18 = distance traveled
paul has traveled

6) 25 × 1.18 = 29.5
$$1945.60$$
$$+ 29.50$$
$$1975.10$$

7) x =
   y =

distance traveled × 1.18 =

Assessment questions

In answering these questions, remember that Paul's odometer gives readings that are consistently too low.

1. Paul continues to cycle round the track, doing a total of 60 laps.
   Copy and complete the table below. (Use a calculator.)

Number of laps	0	10	20	30	40	50	60
Distance Paul *really* travels (km)	0	4	8	12	16	20	24
Distance odometer *says* Paul travels (km)	0	3.40	6.80	10.20	13.60	17.00	20.40

2. Draw a graph to show how the distance shown by the odometer is related to the real distance traveled.
   Label your axes as shown below. Is the graph a straight line? Yes!

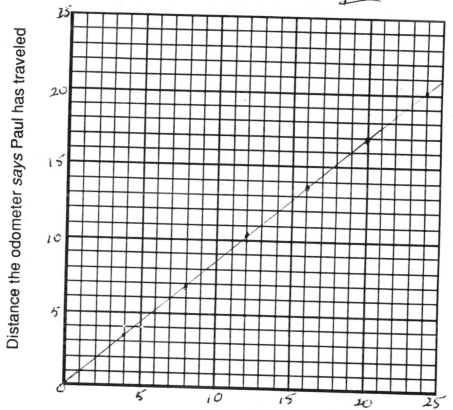

Distance Paul has *really* traveled

* All final answers are boxed *

actual (Because these #'s come out even on the chart)

3) @ $\dfrac{20}{17}$ = $\boxed{.85}$

odometer

When Paul travels 1 Km, his odometer says he has traveled .85 Km.

b) $\dfrac{1}{.85}$ = 1.176470588 km   # of Km odometer says

* rounded to the nearest thousandth.

how much the odometer is off by

When Pauls odometer says he has traveled 1 Km, he has actually traveled 1.176*Km.

4) When Pauls odometer says he has traveled 1960.00 Km, he has actually traveled 2305.882* km

5)   x = what odometer reads
     y = actual distance traveled.

formula $\frac{x}{.85} = y$ (or .85y = x – if you want to find out
                               what his odometer will read (x) given
                               how far he traveled (y))

                    (using same variables as in #5)
6)   .85y = x –(Because   we know the distance that Paul
                 wants to travel and   we want to find out what
                 his   odometer   will   say)

     .85(25) = x   21.75 what his odometer already read
              x = 21.75   +1945.6   ┌─────────────────────┐
                                   ─────────   │ His   odometer will │
                                    1966.85   │ read 1966.85.   │
                                                    └─────────────────────┘

                                    (using same variables as in #5)
7) ┌──────────────────┐
    │ .85y = x   │
    │ .85(25) = 21.25   │
    │   +1945.6   │ – what   his odometer already reads
    │   1966.85   │
    └──────────────────┘

8) No. The   correct   statement   should   be:

    ┌──┐
    │ Paul's odometer has a 15% error   │
    └──┘

Design a tent

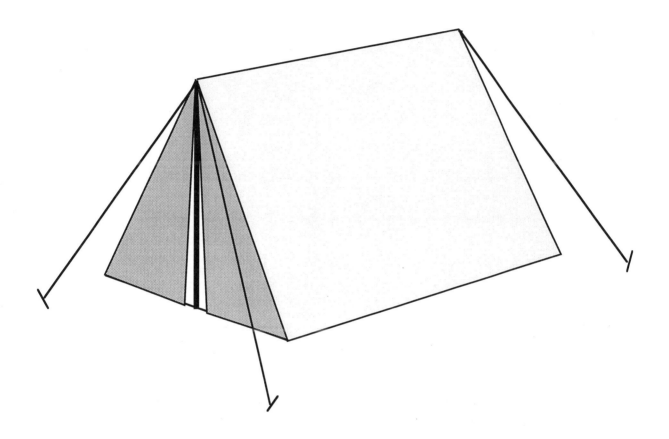

Task Description

Grade Level: High

Students are asked to design a tent, making estimates for suitable dimensions. Explain that if students want to, they may find it helpful to make paper models of their experimental designs to check that they work. A supply of scissors and paper should be available if students request them.

> *Estimate dimensions.*
>
> *Visualize and sketch a net for a tent.*
>
> *Calculate measurements using the Pythagorean theorem and/or the trigonometric ratios.*

Assumed Mathematical Background

Students should have experience of estimation, drawing nets of 3-D objects, using the Pythagorean Theorem and/or the trigonometric ratios.

Core Elements of Performance

This task provides students with the opportunity to:

- estimate dimensions of an adult that would need to fit into the tent.
- visualize and sketch what the net of a tent looks like.
- calculate measurements and label the sketch.
- apply the Pythagorean Theorem.
- apply the trigonometric ratios.

Circumstances

Grouping: Students work individually or in pairs. Pair work should encourage discussion. Each member of a pair, however, must produce his or her own written solution.

Materials: Each pair of students will need a scientific calculator. Students may request a pair or scissors and some paper for model making.

Estimated time: 45 minutes

Design a tent

The aim of this assessment is to provide the opportunity for you to:
- *estimate dimensions of a person.*
- *visualize and sketch a net for a tent, showing all the measurements.*

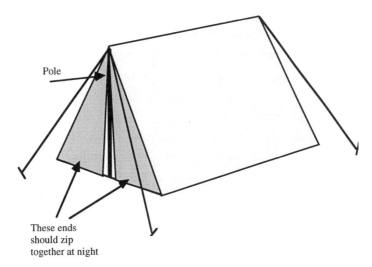

Pole

These ends
should zip
together at night

Your task is to design a tent like the one in the picture.

Your design must satisfy these conditions:

> - It must be big enough for two adults to sleep in (with their baggage).
>
> - It must be big enough for someone to move around in while kneeling down.
>
> - The bottom of the tent will be made from a thick rectangle of plastic.
>
> - The sloping sides and the two ends will be made from a single, large sheet of canvas. (It should be possible to cut the canvas so that the two ends do not need sewing onto the sloping sides. It should be possible to zip up the ends at night.)
>
> - Two vertical tent poles will hold the whole tent up.

1. Estimate the relevant dimensions of a typical adult and write these down.

2. Estimate the dimensions you will need for the rectangular plastic base.

   Estimate the length of the vertical tent poles you will need.
   Explain how you get these measurements.

3. Draw a sketch to show how you will cut the canvas from a single piece.
   Show all the measurements clearly.
   Calculate any lengths or angles you don't know.
   Explain how you figured out these lengths and angles.

A Sample Solution

1. The height and width of typical U.S. males and females are given in the table below, together with the range within which approximately 90% of the population lie.

	Average	Range
Males: Height	1740mm / 5' 9"	1625 - 1855mm / 5' 4" - 6' 2"
Males: Width	460mm / 1' 6 "	415 - 510 mm / 1' 4" - 1' 8"
Females: Height	1610mm / 5' 4"	1505 - 1710 mm / 4' 11" - 5' 8"
Females: Width	415mm / 1' 4"	370 - 460 mm / 1' 3" - 1' 6"

Accept any answer therefore that lies between
Height 5' 4" to 6' 2"; Width 1' 4" to 2'; Kneeling height 4' to 4'6".

2. It would thus seem sensible to design the plastic base to be at least 6' 6" in length and at least 4 feet wide. More would be better for baggage.

3. The length of the tent poles have to lie between the above height and kneeling height.

4. In the drawing below, the tent is made to fit a base L units long and W units wide with tent poles of height H units.

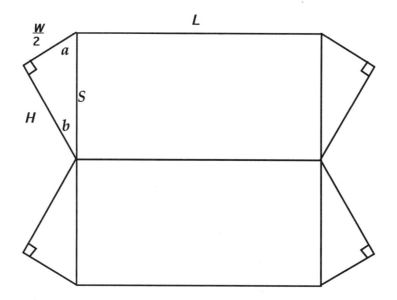

The dimension labeled S may be found using the Pythagorean theorem.

The angles labeled a and b may be found using trigonometric ratios.

About this task

Use the following script:

"This task asks you to design a tent like the one in the picture. Read the conditions through carefully. You can use measurements in feet, inches, meters or centimeters - whichever you prefer."

This section offers a characterization of student responses and provides indications of the ways in which the students were successful or unsuccessful in engaging with and completing the task. The descriptions are keyed to the Core Elements of Performance. Our global descriptions of student work range from, "The student needs significant instruction," to, "The student's work meets the essential demands of the task." Samples of student work that exemplify these descriptions of performance are included below, accompanied by commentary on central aspects of each student's response. These sample responses are *representative*; they may not mirror the global description of performance in all respects, being weaker in some and stronger in others.

The characterization of student responses for this task is based on these Core Elements of Performance:

- estimate dimensions of an adult that would need to fit into the tent.
- visualize and sketch what the net of a tent looks like.
- calculate measurements and label the sketch.
- apply the Pythagorean Theorem.
- apply the trigonometric ratios.

Descriptions of student work

The student needs significant instruction

Typically, the student understands the prompt and attempts to estimate dimensions and draw diagrams. The student is unable to produce satisfactory estimates or coordinate the constraints in the problem. The student may attempt to transfer measurements to a drawing of the base of the tent, but is unable to visualize how the top may be constructed.

Student A

Student A has made reasonable estimates of the dimensions of a typical adult. The student has drawn a tent base which is somewhat small, and although the response justifies the fact that 6 feet will be long enough, it ignores the need for space for baggage. The length of the tent poles is again adequate and the net for the canvas is drawn satisfactorily. The right angle can be inferred from the subsequent use of the Pythagorean theorem. In using the theorem, however, the response has rounded down to 4.2 feet for the slant height. This would make the canvas very tight!

The student needs some instruction

Typically the student attempts to satisfy some but not all of the constraints in the problem. Some reasonable estimates are made. The student attempts to show how the tent may be constructed and transfers some measurements correctly to a drawing. There is no attempt to calculate new lengths or angles.

Student B

Student B has correctly estimated the dimensions of a typical adult and designed an appropriate plastic base for the tent. The dimensions are transferred correctly to the plan but the response has not identified the right angle at the base of the zip correctly. The student gains credit for realizing that the Pythagorean theorem is appropriate but gains no credit for using it incorrectly selecting the wrong side as the hypotenuse. No attempt has been made to calculate angles.

The student's work needs to be revised

Typically, the student attempts to satisfy all constraints in the problem. The student attempts to show how the tent may be constructed and transfers measurements correctly to a drawing. The student selects and uses appropriate mathematical techniques to calculate new lengths or angles.
A suitable tent could not yet be successfully constructed from the plan.

Student C

Student C has unusually mixed the units, which makes assessment difficult! The estimates for question 1 are satisfactory. (The person is 6 feet high, 50 cm wide.) The metric estimate for a person's height as 198 cm is, however, too large (in Question 2) and since there are now two conflicting estimates the response gains no credit for the person's height. The student does, however, estimate a realistic kneeling height of 148 cm (under the answer to question 2). The response has taken account of the room needed for baggage in the design of the base.

The tent design is well drawn, although the response has ignored the fact that the base was to be made from a different material. Student C has (correctly) shown the length as 195 cm (= 6' 5"), and has transferred the pole length 148 cm and the semi-width 75 cm correctly to the diagram. The attempt to use the Pythagorean theorem implies that the student has recognized the correct right angle, but the calculation of the slant height is incorrect (it should be 165 cm). Again, no attempt has been made to calculate angles.

The student's work meets the essential demands of the task

Typically, the student satisfies all constraints in the problem. The student shows how the tent may be constructed and transfers all measurements correctly to a drawing. Appropriate mathematical techniques have been used to calculate new lengths and angles. These calculations are mostly correct. A suitable tent could be constructed from the plan.

Student D

In question 1, Student D has made estimates for the height and width of a typical person which are within the acceptable range. The estimate for kneeling height, which is embedded in the response to question 3, is also acceptable.

The responses to questions 2 and 3 allow space for luggage and moving around.

The sketch showing the dimensions of the tent is correct and the sloping side of the tent has been correctly calculated using the Pythagorean theorem.

No attempt has been made to calculate the angles of the triangle but this is not essential since a triangle is uniquely determined if the lengths of the three sides are known.

Student A

Design a tent

We Started with a triangular type of tent.

- The bottom of the tent is made from thick rectangle of plastic.

- The Sloping Sides and the two ends will be made from a Single Sheet of Canvas.

1. The relevant dimensions of a typical adult is.

height = 6ft

width = 1.5ft

2. dimensions for a rectangular base:

3ft

6ft

This is because the length of a normal person is 6' and the width is 1.5' because we need people to sleep in it, it will be twice the width of one person (people usually don't Sleep Stretched out).

3. length of tents poles =

4' and 6'

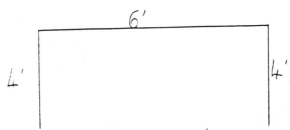

We took the average measurment of a person and put them on our poles eg. 6' = length and a kneeling-down person is aproximally 4' so this is the height.

4.

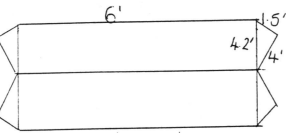

We used Pythagoras theory to work out the sloping Side = 4·2'

Design a tent Pt 2.

base :

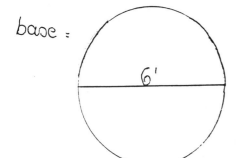

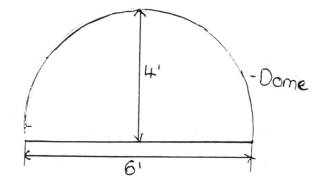

The tent base is 6' diametre, this is as big as an average adult. The height of the tent is used because of the same reasons of the previous tent.

Design a Tent

1. Size typical adult ^TALL 6ft x ^WIDE 2ft

2. 6ft wide & 8ft long
   2 extra feet in the length & 2 extra feet in
   width more than average person two people
   to give room in between the people

3. Length of the Poles   5'

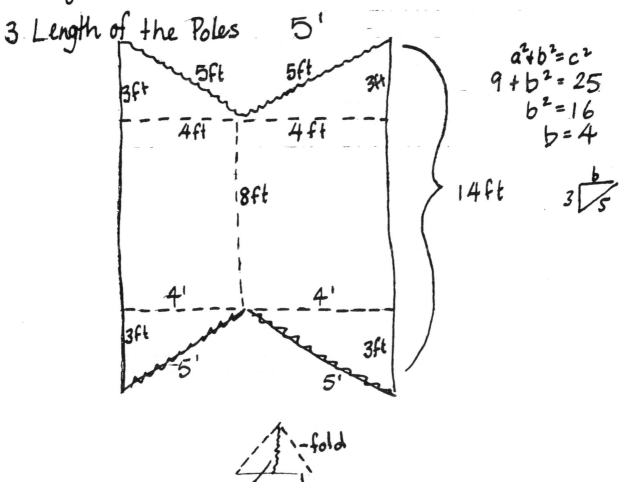

$$a^2 + b^2 = c^2$$
$$9 + b^2 = 25$$
$$b^2 = 16$$
$$b = 4$$

Student C

1   6 foot high . 50cm wide.

2   6 foot 5 inch . 150cm wide . We got the average height which is around 5'9" to 6" so we made it 6 foot 5 inches to allow room for sleeping bags and camping mats which are generally longer than who sleeps on them.

Sleeping bags are roughly 50 cm accross layed flat so we doubled that then added 50cm for movement room and for gear.

3. If a person is 198 cm high roughly then there is half a metre from knees to feet then the tent poles must be 198 − 50 = 148 cm high.

4

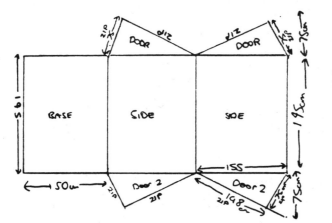

FINISH NET

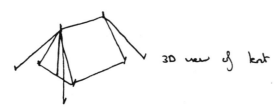

This is to workout the vertical side of the door using pythagorus and it is also the same scale as the net above by putting in the base and using a compass to work out where the sides meet and then measuring the line from top to the centre of the base width.

$x^2 = 5625$

$24025 + 5625 = \sqrt{29650} =$

30 view of tent

1) 6 ft. tall - 2 ft. wide ; The typical person is 6ft. Tall. You are about 1½ ft. wide and you have to include their broad shoulders.

2) 7 ft. long 5ft wide ; You want a little bit more room than they are tall incase they move around. The width is doubled for two people plus a little more room cause they don't want to be squished right next to eachother!

3) The length of the vertical tent poles is about 4½ feet tall. A six foot person is about 4 feet on their knees and can move around easily.

4)

on back → need more time.

I needed about 15 more minutes to write how I got the measurements.

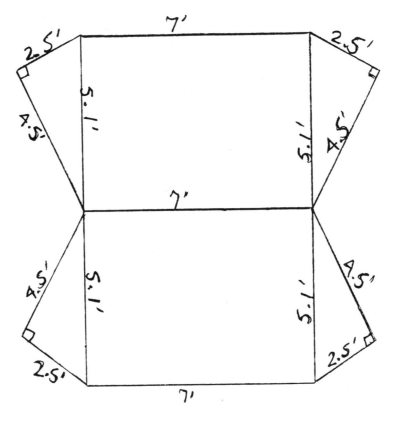

$4.5^1 + 2.5^7 =$

$20.25 + 6.25 =$

26.5

$\sqrt{26}5 = 5.1$

2500% Blowup

Task Description

Grade Level: Secondary

Students are presented with a copy of a full page ad for 35 mm camera film from a magazine. The ad shows a photograph and a blowup of part of this photograph. It claims, "You're looking at a 2500% blowup ..." .

Students are asked to make measurements and calculations that demonstrate that the blowup is in fact 2500%.

> *Understand the meaning of a "2500% blowup" of a picture.*
>
> *Work with the idea of enlargement by a given factor.*

Assumed Mathematical Background

Students should have had some experience with the concept of percent enlargement of a figure, and with the idea of similar figures. (Enlargement of a figure produces a figure similar to the original, one with the same proportions.) They should also have had experience doing non-routine problems.

Core Elements of Performance

- Know that a "2500% blowup" means something enlarged by a factor of 25.

- Know that uniformly enlarged figures are "similar" to the original (have the same proportions as the original).

- Be able to make precise measurements with a ruler.

- Understand the difference between a factor of enlargement based on linear dimensions and one based on area.

- Appreciate that when something is enlarged in stages, the total enlargement is the *product* of the individual enlargements).

Circumstances

Grouping: Students work in pairs. Each submits a separate paper.

Materials: pencil, paper, ruler (to measure in millimeters), calculator

Estimated time: 45 minutes

Acknowledgments

The advertisement is from *Natural History* magazine.

2500% Blowup

The aim of this assessment is to provide the opportunity for you to:

- *show the meaning of "2500% blowup" of a picture.*
- *use mathematics to verify a claim made in an advertisement.*

The next page shows a copy of a magazine ad for film.

There is a small photo in the upper right corner.
The rest of the picture is a blowup of part of that photo.

An important fact (not stated in the ad) is that the small photo is itself a blowup from a negative which measures 24 mm by 35 mm.

The ad claims that there is a 2500% blowup.
This claim is actually correct.

Your task is to show that linear measurements on the blowup are 2500% larger than linear measurements on the negative.

You will have to:
- make careful measurements on the photo and on its blowup.
- take into account the size of the negative.
- make calculations based on these measurements.
- use the results of these calculations to arrive at the 2500% blowup figure.

Be sure to explain your reasoning, using diagrams, formulas, and whatever else is useful to communicate the ideas.

A Sample Solution

(Note: The solution depends on the following fact. If something is enlarged by a factor of F_1, and then the enlargement is itself enlarged by a factor of F_2, the total enlargement is by a factor of $F_1 F_2$.)

The small picture in the upper right hand corner measures about 75 mm by 112 mm. If this is a direct blowup from a 24 mm by 35 mm negative, the enlargement factor on the short side would be $75/24 \approx 3.125$, while the enlargement factor on the long side would be $112/35 \approx 3.2$. Since these factors are close to one another, it makes sense to assume that the small picture is a blowup of the full negative. We will assume the factor of enlargement is about 3.16.

(This is a factor of enlargement for the **linear** dimensions of the figure. We will have to see if this makes sense in the context of the claim of the ad, rather than an enlargement factor for increase of the **area** of the picture.)

It is a little bit harder to determine how much bigger the enlargement is than the small picture in the upper right hand corner. But here is one way:

The horizontal top of the banner (just above the player's head) measures 18 mm in the small picture, and 140 mm in the blowup. That is an enlargement factor of $140/18 \approx 7.78$.

As another determination of the enlargement factor, the height of the player from the bottom of his feet to the top of his head measures about 13 mm in the small picture and about 101 mm in the enlargement. That is an enlargement factor of about $101/13 \approx 7.77$.

Since these two factors are close, it make sense to use one of them, say 7.77, as an estimate of the enlargement factor from the small picture to the enlargement.

The **total** enlargement is the product of these:

$$(3.16)\,(7.7) \approx 24.33.$$

Thus the total enlargement (from the negative to the enlarged picture) is by a factor of about 24.3. Rounded to two figures and converted to percent this would be 2400%.

The conclusion is that, while the ad might have exaggerated a little, in general the claim that there is a 2500% blowup is reasonable. It should be emphasized that it is difficult to make accurate measurements here, and not much weight should be attached to the difference between a factor of 24 and a factor of 25.

For Formal Assessment

It may be a good idea to have a discussion with students about film negatives and prints made from them on a day before they attempt the task. The most common type of film, "35 mm" film, has rectangular negatives that measure about 24 mm by 35 mm. If a "contact" print is made from a negative there is no enlargement, but most film processors these days enlarge all the prints from the negative by a factor of about 3 or 4. If there is further blowup to "an enlargement" it is often by another factor 2 or 3.

Students should understand these basic facts about film, but should not be told specifically about how to solve the task.

Extensions

2500% Blowup can be extended in several ways.

One is to explore successive enlargements on a photocopy machine to get a more direct experience with the idea that enlargement factors are **multiplied** when there are successive enlargements.

Another might be to explore actual film enlargement procedures to resolve the following dilemma:
35 mm film with its 24 mm by 35 mm negatives is a very common film used in this country. Yet the prints one gets from the negative are often described (in inches) as 3" by 5", 4" by 6", 8" by 10", and so on. The dilemma is not that there is a conflict between inches and millimeters, but that these ratios are all different:

$$24/35 \approx 0.69 \qquad 3/5 = 0.60 \qquad 4/6 \approx 0.67 \qquad 8/10 = 0.80$$

Is there distortion in the blowup? Or are parts of the negative cut off in the enlargements? If so, which parts?

This section offers a characterization of student responses and provides indications of the ways in which the students were successful or unsuccessful in engaging with and completing the task. The descriptions are keyed to the Core Elements of Performance. Our global descriptions of student work range from, "The student needs significant instruction," to, " The student's work meets the essential demands of the task." Samples of student work that exemplify these descriptions of performance are included below, accompanied by commentary on central aspects of each student's response. These sample responses are *representative*; they may not mirror the global description of performance in all respects, being weaker in some and stronger in others.

The characterization of student responses for this task is based on these Core Elements of Performance:

- know that a "2500% blowup" means something enlarged by a factor of 25.

- know that uniformly enlarged figures are "similar" to the original (have the same proportions as the original).

- be able to make precise measurements with a ruler.

- understand the difference between a factor of enlargement based on linear dimensions and one based on area.

- appreciate that when something is enlarged in stages, the total enlargement is the *product* of the individual enlargements).

- appreciate that when something is enlarged in stages, the total enlargement is the *product* of the individual enlargements).

Descriptions of student work

The student needs significant instruction

These papers show at most evidence of clear understanding of at least one of the facts required to solve the problem.

Typically the response shows that they know that 2500% means increase by a factor of 25.

Student A

This response shows that it is to work from the negative to the small picture. It states that it will multiply the dimensions of the negative by 25 and then compute the area. There is some attempt to deal with ratios but this is limited and not articulated clearly.

The student needs some instruction

These papers provide evidence that the student knows that a factor of enlargement is found by computing the ratio of a length in the enlarged picture to the corresponding length in the original.

Student B

This response shows that the student knows to compute the ratio of a length in the negative to the corresponding length in the little picture. It also shows that the student knows to compute the ratio of a length in the small picture to the corresponding length in the large picture. However, the student adds these two factors of enlargement to find the overall enlargement. This is a conceptual error. The factors of enlargement must be multiplied and NOT added.

The student's work needs to be revised

Aspects of these papers show that the student has the mathematical power to accomplish the task.

The student understands that two factors of enlargement must be combined somehow to arrive at the net enlargement claimed in the add. However, the student does NOT demonstrate a serious misunderstanding by adding the factors of enlargement by adding rather than multiplying the factors of enlargement.

Student C

This student arrives at the correct result of a net enlargement by a factor of about 25, but does so in a somewhat roundabout manner. In particular the student does not find the individual factors of enlargement for each stage.

The student's work meets the essential demands of the task

Almost all aspects of the response are correct.

Typically the student finds correctly the two individual factors of enlargement, and shows that their product is approximately 25.

Student D

This response fully accomplishes the task. The two individual factors of enlargement are found, and the student shows that their product is approximately 25.

A number of additional aspects makes this an exceptional response. One is the style of communication. The integration of calculations, diagrams, and relevant prose creates a delightfully articulated piece. Another is the discussion of error and the exploration of upper and lower bounds.

Student A

Negative

$35 \text{ mm} \times 25$

840 mm^2 $24 \text{ mm} \times 25$

In order to find the 2500% of the negative you multiple each dementiion by 25. You have to find the percent of the smaller picture and find a lenth that is found in both pictures and compare it to one each other.

875 m

600 mm | 2500%

35

24

$840 \div 8250$

75 mm | 110 mm^3
small picture
8250 mm^2

$24 : 75$ $\dfrac{24}{75} : \dfrac{35}{110}$ $\dfrac{110}{35} = 17$

$35 : 110$

$\dfrac{}{110}$

bench

| 35

$\dfrac{12}{38}$

$\dfrac{6}{19}$

$\dfrac{19}{6} = \dfrac{22}{7}$ $6 : 19 =$ $7 : 22 = 7$

The 2500% Blow up

In doing this problem I determined that the photo in the add was indeed a 2500% blow up of the little photo in the corner. I just measured a object in the little picture and then one in the larger picture and it was 23 times larger (I had determined that the little picture was a 200% blow up)

The problem we were asked to solve was to show that the big picture was a 2500% blow up from the negative. The problem and the two pictures are included in appendix A of this report.

My approach to this problem was probably a pretty common one. I took the two pictures, a ruler and thought about it for a while. I determined that if it was a 2500% blow up than everything in the negative had to be 25 times smaller. So I measured the dimensions of the little picture and came up with 5.5 X 8. This was about 2 times that of the negative, so thus a 200% blow up. So I then looked for a object to measure in the picture to determine how much it was blown up. I measured the back of one of the seats right above the football players head and determined that the seat was 2 cm long in the large photo. It was .09 cm approximately in the little picture. Since I determined that the little picture was 2 times the size of the negative I could concur that the large picture would then be 23 times the size of the little picture. I did the math and .09 times 23 is approximately 2 cm. So since this dimension is 25 times the size of the negative I conclude that the picture must be 25 times the size of the negative and therefore a 2500% blow up.

I have confidence in my solution because this is the way that many other class mates have solved the problem and I measured another object in the picture and the length was similar. I think that you have to measure a 1 dimensional object though to get a accurate measurement, like a line or something.

My results were that it is a 2500% blow up because images in it are 25 times the size of images in the negative.

I think that measuring and mathematically comparing angles is a very important part of any trade that deals with engineering, building ect. If you have dimensions and want to make a scale model this kind of thinking is extremely important.

original
picture

113mm.

football player
13mm.

77mm

} take ratios of $\frac{77}{74}$ and $\frac{113}{35}$ to find
hight of football player

negative:

35mm.

4.05mm

24mm

$$\frac{24}{77} = \frac{x}{113}$$

$$77x = 312$$

big blow up:

football player

108 mm.

One can not figure out the % blow up using the edges of the picture, so we used the football player since one can see him completely in both the small blow up and the large blow up.

In the small bu, the measurements of the picture are 113 x 77 mm. In the negative, the measurements are 35 x 24 mm. The football player is 4.05 mm and in the original, 13mm. I divided 4.05 into 103, and got 25.432; therefore growing 2543%.

At first, I didn't understand the situation, and was baffled. But after about 30 seconds, I realized the problem and the way of solving it became apparent immediately. Overall, I thought that the problem was pretty easy.

In this problem I was asked to prove that the Large photo is a 2500% blow up from the small photo, noting the fact that the small photo was printed from a negative that measures 24mm by 35 mm. Also, to understand & verify the claim by the advertisement.

Before I started measurements, I thought about what 2500% exactly meant. It means that the large picture is 25 times as large as the negative:

(how many times)

$$2500\% = ?$$

$$2500\% / 100 = 25 \text{ times}$$

Having established this, I then made measurements on the small photo:

35mm — neg. (24 mm)   88 mm — 59 mm

} I choose to compare the measurements of (neg) 24 mm → (sm. photo) 59 mm, one side of measurements,

(times)

I figured that the sm photo was 2.29x as large as the negative:

• you ask - how many 24mm are in 59 mm?

∴ $59 \div 24 = 2.45$ times

Next I looked at the relationship between the small photo and the large photo. But, since the large photo is on a blow up of the portion of the small photo, I had to pick a section of the small photo that was proportionate to the Large photo. I choose the line from the middle of the head to the right end of the helmet. So, I measured this line in the large picture, and measured the same line in the small picture. Now, I know this is the area where there is room for much error. This is because the small picture is so small that it is difficult to get an exact measurement, it must be noted that being off by just one mm. can throw the percentage off. With this observation, I cannot expect to get an exact 2550%, but something close to it.

I ask myself { So, how many times as large is the Lg photo than the sm photo? how many 9mm are there in 88m? :

$$88 \div 9 = 9.77 \text{ times}$$

Now, I step back and look at all my info:

2.45 times

9.77 times

how many times is the neg. enlarged:

$$2.45 \times 9.77 = 23.9555 \text{ time}$$

So, even though my answer is not exact it is very close. One should realize that there is room for error when working with such a small photo. Also in advertising, the advertiser probably will not claim that the photo is a 2395.55555 % blow up. The advertiser will just round up and claim a 2500% blow up.

To try and make my answer more clear & exact, I decided to show that there is room for error when measuring by using $\pm$ 1mm. Using $\pm$ will allow me to go to the extremes of the number of times and then calculate the percentages:

negative to the small photo is : 2.45 times

sm picture to Lg picture   : 88mm $\pm$ 1 mm $\left.\begin{array}{l} 88+1=89 \\ \overline{9-1-8} \end{array}\right.$

      9 mm $\pm$ 1 mm $\left.\begin{array}{l} 88-1=\overline{87} \\ 9+1=\overline{10} \end{array}\right.$

⟨11.125 Times⟩ or ⟨8.7 Times⟩

Now I figured out the number of times for both and took an average:

11.125 × 2.45 = 27.25625 times ⎫ average : 24.285625

8.7 × 2.45 = 21.315 times ⎬   times.

This shows how much 1 mm can offset the number of times, therefore offsetting the percentage.

I also looked at this problem from an advertisers point of view. I rounded everything up →

because that is what they would probably do:

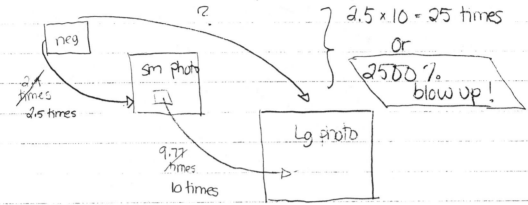

2.5 × 10 = 25 times

or

2500 %
blow up !

neg

?

sm photo

Lg photo

2.5 times

9.77 times

10 times

Now that I have proved that it is (approximately) a 2500 % blow up from the negative to the large photo, one can say that the ad was misleading. It makes one think that the blow up is from the small photo, but really it is from the negative to the lg photo.

Kidney Stones

Task Description

Grade Level: High

This task starts by showing part of an article that gives both the proportion of Americans who have a certain disease and the proportion of Americans with this disease who are male.

The task then asks students to show how these two proportions interact to give the proportion of American males with the disease, and the proportion of American females with the disease.

> *Interpret a statement from an article in a health newsletter.*
>
> *Answer questions about proportions given information in the article.*
>
> *Distinguish part-part and part-whole relationships.*

Assumed Mathematical Background

Students should have had some experience working with parts of a whole expressed as proportions.

Core Elements of Performance

- Work with parts of a whole expressed as proportions.
- Deal with three kinds of cases.
    - Cases where two proportions need to be multiplied.
    - Cases where two proportions need to be added or subtracted.
    - Cases where two proportions need to be divided.
- Represent parts of a whole as circle graphs.
- Generalize a situation using symbols instead of specific numbers.

Circumstances

Grouping: Students work in pairs. Each submits a separate paper.

Materials: pencil, paper, graph paper, ruler, protractor, calculator

Estimated time: 45 minutes

Acknowledgments

The figures in this task came from the UC Berkeley Wellness Letter, August, 1993.

Kidney Stones

The aim of this assessment is to provide the opportunity for you to:

- *interpret information from an article.*
- *use given information about proportions to find other information.*

This statement appeared in a newsletter on health:

> *About one in 10 Americans eventually develops a kidney stone.*
> *Four out of five stone formers are men.*

People who develop a kidney stone are called "stone formers".
In terms of proportions, the newsletter says that:
- The proportion of Americans who are stone formers is **0.1**.
- The proportion of stone formers who are men is **0.8**.

Problem 1
a. What proportion of American **men** eventually develop a kidney stone?

b. What proportion of American **women** eventually develop a kidney stone?

Show how you arrived at your answers.
(You may assume that half of all Americans are men.)

Problem 1 is the heart of this task.
Related problems appear on the following page.
If you have trouble with problem 1, start to work problems 2 and 3 first.
This will help with problem 1.

Related problems:

2. What proportion of Americans are:

   a. men who eventually develop a kidney stone?

   b. men who never develop a kidney stone?

   c. women who eventually develop a kidney stone?

   d. women who never develop a kidney stone?

   Explain your reasoning.
   (You may assume that half of all Americans are men.)

3. What should the four proportions in #2 add up to, and why?
   Draw an accurate circle graph that illustrates these four categories.

Extension

   Suppose that a proportion **p** of Americans eventually develop heart disease, and that a proportion **q** of heart disease patients are men.

4. Say, in terms of **p** and **q**

   a. What proportion of American men eventually develop heart disease?

   b. What proportion of American women eventually develop heart disease?

   (In working this problem, think about how you answered problem 1 above.)

5. In terms of **p** and **q** , say what proportion of Americans are:

   a. men who eventually develop heart disease.

   b. men who never develop heart disease.

   c. women who eventually develop heart disease.

   d. women who never develop heart disease.

   Do these proportions sum to the right number?

   (In working this problem, think about how you answered problem 2 above.)

6. Check your answers in #4 and #5 by substituting the numbers from the first part of this task and seeing if you get the same results.

A Sample Solution

1a. The answer is **0.16**.
Here is a way to think about this. Take a typical 100 Americans.
Of these, 10 are stone formers (one out of ten Americans is a stone former).
Of the 10 stone formers, 8 are men (four out of five stone formers are men).
But also, out of these 100 Americans, 50 are men.
This means that 8 out of these 50 men are stone formers.
Since this selection is typical, 8/50 or **0.16** of American men are stone formers.

   In effect, this thinking involves taking a **ratio** of two **proportions**:
   The proportion of all American men who are stone formers =
   $$\frac{\text{the proportion of stone formers who are men}}{\text{the proportion of Americans who are men}} = \frac{.08}{.5} = .16 \ .$$

1b. The answer is **0.04**. The same reasoning is used:
   The proportion of all American women who are stone formers =
   $$\frac{\text{the proportion of stone formers who are women}}{\text{the proportion of Americans who are women}} = \frac{.02}{.5} = .04.$$

2a. Since a proportion 0.1 of all Americans is a stone former, and a proportion .8 of stone formers are male, then a proportion (.1) (.8) = **.08** of Americans are male stone formers.
   These proportions are **multiplied**, since the second proportion .8 is a part of the group (stone formers) identified in the first proportion.

2b. Assuming that a proportion .5 of Americans are men, it follows from 2a that a proportion .5 - .08 = **.42** of Americans are male non-stone formers.
   The important relation here is
   $$.5 = .08 + .42$$
   $$\text{males} = \text{male stone formers} + \text{male non-stone formers}$$

   In this relation the proportions are **added**, and not multiplied as in 2a. This is because the proportion .08 of Americans who are male stone formers and the proportion .42 of Americans who are male non-stone formers are *disjoint* classes, rather than one being part of the other. Their sum is .5 since together they comprise all male Americans.

2c. Similar reasoning can be used for females:
   Since a proportion .1 of all Americans is a stone former, and a proportion .2 of stone formers are female, then a proportion (.1) (.2) = **.02** of Americans are female stone formers.

2d. Assuming that a proportion .5 of Americans are women, then a proportion .5 - .02 = **.48** of Americans are female stone formers.

3. These four proportions, .08, .42, .02, and .48 have a sum of 1 .
    (Expressed as percentages they would have a sum of 100.)
    This is as expected, since together they represent **all** Americans,
    and they divide all Americans into four disjoint categories.

    Here is a circle graph representing the situation.

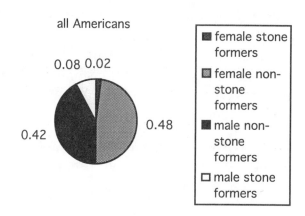

    This particular chart shows all males on the left and all females on the right.

    The number of degrees in each slice is needed for an accurate circle graph
    constructed with a protractor. The number of degrees is found by multiplying
    the proportion by 360°. These numbers are

$$(.08)\,(360°) = 28.8° \qquad (.02)\,(360°) = 7.2°$$
$$(.42)\,(360°) = 151.2° \qquad (.48)\,(360°) = 172.8°$$

Extension

4. Using the reasoning of problem 1:

    a. a proportion $\dfrac{pq}{.5} = \mathbf{2pq}$ of American males eventually develops heart
        disease.

    b. a proportion $\dfrac{p(1\text{-}q)}{.5} = \mathbf{2p(1\text{-}q)}$ of American females eventually develops
        heart disease.

5.   Using the reasoning of question #2:

    a.   For males: A proportion **p** of Americans develop heart disease, and a proportion **q** of these are male. Therefore, a proportion **pq** of Americans are heart disease males.

    b.   Of the proportion .5 of Americans who are males, a proportion **pq** are heart disease males, so a proportion **.5 - pq** are non-heart disease males.

    c.   For females: A proportion **q** of heart disease Americans are male, which means that a proportion **1-q** of heart disease Americans must be female. This in turn means that a proportion **p (1-q)** of Americans are heart disease females.

    d.   Of the proportion .5 of Americans who are females, a proportion **p (1-q)** are heart disease females. It follows that a proportion **.5 - p (1-q)** of Americans are non-heart disease females.

    Summarizing: Of all Americans, a proportion:
        a.   **p q**   are men who eventually develop heart disease.
        b.   **.5 - pq**   are men who never develop heart disease.
        c.   **p (1-q)**   are women who eventually develop heart disease.
        d.   **.5 - p (1-q)** are women who never develop heart disease.
    Regardless of what **p** and **q** are, the algebraic sum of all these proportions is the number 1. This is as it should be, since all Americans fall into one or another of these 4 categories. (Expressed as percentages, all these proportions would be multiplied by 100, and their algebraic sum would be 100.)

6.   For the kidney stones disease, we have **p** = .1, **q** = .8.
    4a.   2 p q   = 2 (.1) (.8)   = .16
    4b.   2 p (1-q)   = 2 (.1) (.2)   = .04
    5a.   p q   = (.1) (.8)   = .08
    5b.   .5 - pq = .5 - (.1) (.8) = .42
    5c.   p (1-q) = (.1) (1-.8)   = .02
    5d.   .5 - p (1-q)   = .5 - (.1) (1-.8)   = .48

For Formal Assessment

This task deals with proportions of Americans who have a certain disease. The article says,

> "One in ten Americans will eventually develop a kidney stone. Four out of five stone formers are men. "

Remind students that proportions are simply ways of expressing parts of a whole. Any proportion can be expressed as a decimal, or as a fraction, or as a percent. For example, the proportion "four out of five" can be expressed in any of these forms:

$$0.8 \qquad \frac{4}{5} \qquad \frac{8}{10} \qquad 80\%$$

The intent behind this task is to see how well students understand typical ways of presenting information about proportions that are used in books, newspapers, and magazines.

Specifically, we are interested in seeing whether students understand, at least intuitively:

- that when two proportions each refer to parts of the same whole, then taking the **ratio** of the proportions shows what proportion the smaller part is of the larger part (problem 1).

- that when one proportion refers to a part of a whole, and another proportion refers to a part of the first part, then **multiplying** the two proportions gives the proportion of the smaller part to the whole (problems 2a and 2c).

- that when two proportions refer to separate parts of a whole, then **adding** the two proportions gives the proportion of both parts together to the whole (problem 2b and 2d).

  Note: In this task the term "**proportion**" is used in the way it is used in the real world. A proportion of a quantity means a definite part or fraction of the quantity; it can be expressed as a number between 0 and 1 (or as a percent between 0 and 100). Many school texts in this country have adopted a definition of proportion based on the classical Greek theory of proportion, namely a *proportion is a statement of equality between two ratios*. This meaning of proportion does not appear outside a school text context.

In the last part (questions 4 and 5) we go on to see if students can generalize some of what they know using symbols like p and q instead of specific numbers to stand for proportions.

This section offers a characterization of student responses and provides indications of the ways in which the students were successful or unsuccessful in engaging with and completing the task. The descriptions are keyed to the Core Elements of Performance. Our global descriptions of student work range from, "The student needs significant instruction," to, "The student's work meets the essential demands of the task." Samples of student work that exemplify these descriptions of performance are included below, accompanied by commentary on central aspects of each student's response. These sample responses are *representative*; they may not mirror the global description of performance in all respects, being weaker in some and stronger in others.

The characterization of student responses for this task is based on these Core Elements of Performance:

- work with parts of a whole expressed as proportions.
- deal with three kinds of cases:
  - cases where two proportions need to be multiplied.
  - cases where two proportions need to be added or subtracted.
  - cases where two proportions need to be divided.
- represent parts of a whole as circle graphs.
- generalize a situation using symbols instead of specific numbers.

Descriptions of student work

The student needs significant instruction

These papers show, at most, evidence that the student can conceptualize the situation in terms of an example: thinking in terms of an average 100 Americans.

Student A

This response states correctly in question 1a that 8 out of 100 Americans are men stone formers, but then goes on to state incorrectly that 8 out of 100 American men are stone formers. This amounts to using an incorrect "whole" for this "part-whole" situation.

The student needs some instruction

These papers provide evidence of multiplication of two proportions to arrive at a proportion representing "a part of a part".

Student B

The response labels clearly each proportion used, but fails to keep clear what the relevant "whole" is in the various part-whole situation.

The student's work needs to be revised

These papers show correct answers for the numerical problems, and have at least minimal explanations. They make some headway on the problems requiring generalization in terms of **p** and **q**, but don't get them fully correct.

Student C

Correct answers to questions 1-3, but the explanations are skimpy. The work presented for questions 4 and 5 is not quite right and needs to be revised.

The student's work meets the essential demands of the task

Typically, these papers may have a few flaws.

Student D

This response is a strong one. The weakest point is the circle graph.

Exceptional responses

Student E

This response is concise, correct, clear and insightful in its explanation. It also has an elegant circle graph.

Student A

Kidney Stone

American stone formers = 0.1

Stone formers who are men = 0.8

Problem 1

a) Amer. Men who develop a kidney stone =

  1) Out of 100 0.1 Americans form a stone = 10

  2) Out of the 0.8 = 8

  3 8:100 American Men Form Kidney stones = 4:50 2:25

b) Amer. Women who develop a kidney stone =

  1). 8 men out of 10 leaves 2 women 2:10 ⁴⁄₅

2) .1 form kidney ston .8 of those are men = $\frac{.1}{.8}$

  a) ~~........~~ $\frac{.1}{.2}$

  c) $\frac{.1}{.2}$

  d) $\frac{.1}{.8}$

3) They should add up to 2 = 100%

women who don't .8 .8 who do
  .2 .2
  woman who do .2 men who don't

4) $\frac{P}{q}$ = ~~.........~~

  b) P – $\frac{P}{q}$

5) Where m = # of men $\frac{P}{q}$ – m =

1.a. The proporation of stone formers who are American men one is
.08   american
          stone formers → (.1)(.8) = .08
                              ↑
                   male stone formers

b The proporation of American women who are stone
  formers is .02   (.1)(.2) = .02.

2a The proporation of Americans who are male stone formers is
  .04 american → (.1)(.5)(.8) = .04
       stone formers
              ↑   ↑
       ½ Americans are men   male stone formers

b The proporation of Americans who are men and never form a stone is
  .46   Americans (.5) - med (.04) = 46
        who are men
                   ↑
              the # who form a stone

c The proporation of Americans who are women and stone formers is
  .01   womin (.5)(.1)(.2) = .01
        American stone formers ↑ women stone formers

d The proporation of Americans who are women and never form a stone is
  .49   A(.5) - (.01) = .49
       ½ Americans are female   # of American female stone formers

3   1 - because we started with Americans as a whole and
     then broke it down into four categories

     sf = stone former
     n = not a stone formers

4a (p)(q)
 b (p)(1-q)

5a (.5)(p)(q)
 b   (.5) - ((.5)(p)(q))
 c (.5)(p)(1-q)
 d (.5) - [(.5)(p)(1-q)]

 6. They work!

① a) .16

b) .04

Ten in every hundred (given)

men 50 8 Amount of men in a hundred
women 50 2 Amount of women in a hundred.

$\frac{8}{50}$ $\frac{2}{50}$

.16   .04

1   Proportion of women with Stones
Proportion of men with Stones

② a) .08   Same as #1 excep
   b) .42   ÷ by 100 total   , Stone growers
   c) .02   Americans
   d) .48

③ 1 = 100%   of Americans

.16 SM   .04 SW

.38 NSM   .46 NSW

④ a 9/50
   b p-9/50

⑤ a 9/100   Same as #2
   b (50-9)/100   More algebra because
   c p-9/100   there are no numbers
   d [50-(p-9)] / 100

Kidney Stones

Problem 1-
a. 16% of American men are stone formers because 8% of all Americans are men who develop them and only half of all Americans are men. So, the amount of men who develop them is 2(8%), or 16%.
b. 4% of all American women develop kidney stones for the same reasons as above.

Problem 2-
a. 8%
b. 42%
c. 2%
d. 48%

Reasoning- The reason these are exactly half of the amount in the previous problem is because the percentages are taken of all Americans, and are not split up into gender.

Problem 3-
The four proportions should, and do, add up to 100%, because they represent the 4 portions (that are relevant to this problem) of the entire population.

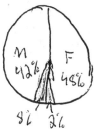

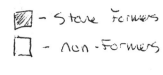

Problem 4-
a. 2pq
b. 2p(1-q)

Problem 5-
a. pq
b. 50%-pq
c. p(1-q)
d. 50%-p(1-q)

These proportions add up to 100%, which is what they should add up to, since it represents the entire population.

Problem 6- The results are all the same. It makes perfect sense because they are the same questions, except for one set is algebraic and the other is numeric.

Student E

1. a) 16% $\Longrightarrow$

   b) 4%

$$\begin{array}{r} .1 \quad \text{Americans} \\ \times\ .8 \quad \text{men} \\ \hline .08 \quad \text{of Americans are men} \times 2 = .16 \text{ men who} \\ \text{have stones} \end{array}$$

2. a) 8%

   b) 42%

   c) 2%

   d) 48%

The percentage of men with stones is twice as much
as the percentages of Americans who are male
"stone formers", because of my assumption that
there are equal number of men as women. All
that is left to do is to subtract the percentage
from 50 (half the population) to get each
non-stone-forming group.

4. a) $2pq$

   b) $2[p - (pq)]$

5. a) pq $\Longrightarrow$ $pq + [.50 - pq] + [p - pq] + [.50 - \{p - (pq)\}]$

   b) $.50 - (pq)$

   c) $p - (pq)$ $\boxed{1}$

   d) $.50 - [p - (pq)]$ Yes, these proportions add up
                             to the right number. (1)

3. These four proportions should add up to 100%, the total American population.

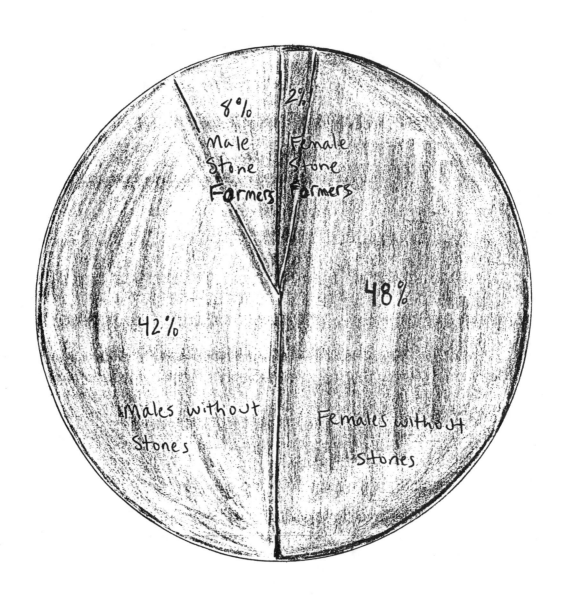

Packaging a soda bottle

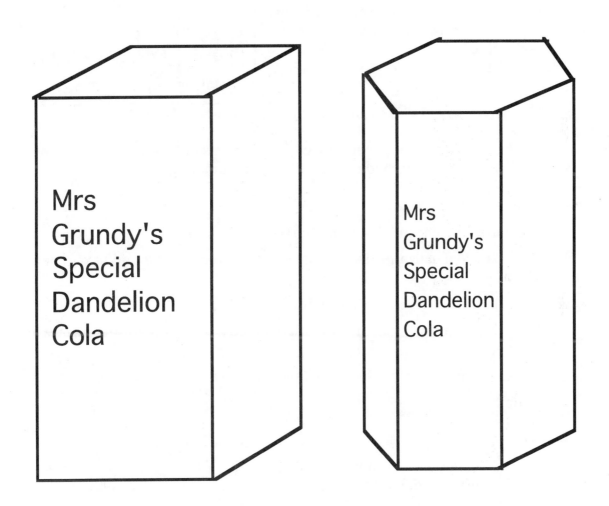

Mrs Grundy's Special Dandelion Cola

Mrs Grundy's Special Dandelion Cola

Task Description

Grade Level: High

In this task students are asked to sketch the net for two boxes, including all the measurements. The first is a rectangular solid, while the second is hexagonal in cross section. In the latter case, a little scale drawing, use of Pythagorean theorem or trigonometry is needed in order to calculate the relevant dimensions. Students who have difficulty in visualizing the nets may like to try to make the boxes as they proceed, but this will considerably extend the task length.

> *Measure accurately.*
>
> *Draw nets of rectangular and hexagonal prisms.*
>
> *Use the Pythagorean theorem or trigonometry to find the dimensions of the nets.*
>
> *Estimate how many nets fit onto a piece of cardboard.*
>
> *Justify computations.*

Assumed Mathematical Background

It is assumed that students have experience of drawing nets of 3-D shapes, using the Pythagorean theorem or the trigonometric ratios, and estimating.

Core Elements of Performance

- Measure a drawing accurately in centimeters and millimeters.
- Use their spatial visualization skills to draw nets of rectangular and hexagonal prisms.
- Visualize the way in which the nets will be glued together.
- Use the Pythagorean theorem or some trigonometry in solving for the surface area of each net.
- Estimate the number of box nets that would fit onto a 1m x 1m sized cardboard.
- Justify their computations.

Circumstances

Grouping: Students work individually or in pairs. Pair work should encourage discussion. Each member has his or her own written solution.

Materials: Each student will need to be given the task prompt, several plain sheets of paper, a 30 centimeter ruler and a calculator.

                 Please note that graph paper and geometric dotted paper should not be issued, as these imply to students that accurate drawings should be made.

Estimated time: 1 hour

Task 6090

Packaging a soda bottle

The aim of this assessment is to provide the opportunity for you to:
- *measure accurately.*
- *sketch the nets of 3-D shapes showing dimensions.*
- *find the surface area of each net.*
- *estimate how many nets can be cut from a piece of cardboard.*
- *justify your computations.*

Top View

Mrs
Grundy's
Special
Dandelion
Cola

Side view

Mrs. Grundy wants to package her homemade cola bottles in boxes.

Above is an accurate full size drawing of the top and side views of her bottle.

There are two possible box designs she may use.

One has a square top and one has a hexagonal top.

These boxes must be a tight fit, or the bottles will rattle around when they are being transported.

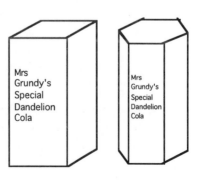

1. Sketch diagrams to show how you would make each box from a single piece of card. You do not need to do this accurately.

   Show where you would put flaps for gluing each box together.

2. By measuring the drawing of the bottle in centimeters, figure out the length of *every* edge of each box in centimeters.

   Show how you figured these lengths out.

   On your diagrams for question 1, write down these lengths.

3. Calculate the amount of cardboard used by each design in square centimeters.

   Show how you figured this out.

4. Suppose you had a sheet of card 1 meter long and 1 meter wide.

   Estimate the number of 'square top' boxes that could be made from a single sheet. Explain your reasoning fully.

   Estimate the number of 'hexagon top' boxes that could be made from a single sheet. Explain your reasoning fully.

A Sample Solution

The measurements in the following diagrams are given to the nearest millimeter.

They are the minimum measurements acceptable.

1. Measurements 1 mm greater than these are acceptable. Beyond that the bottle will tend to rattle around too much! The positions of the tabs for glue may be varied from those shown, but must be in sensible positions.

2. The calculation of the side of one hexagon may be done using scale drawing, the Pythagorean theorem, or by trigonometry. It will result in a hexagon of side length $\sqrt{12} = 3.5$ cm to the nearest mm.

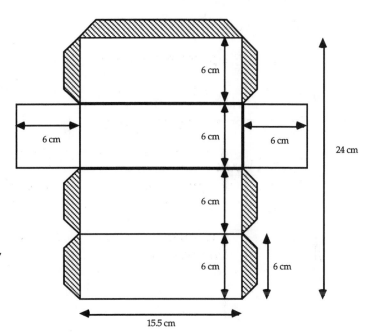

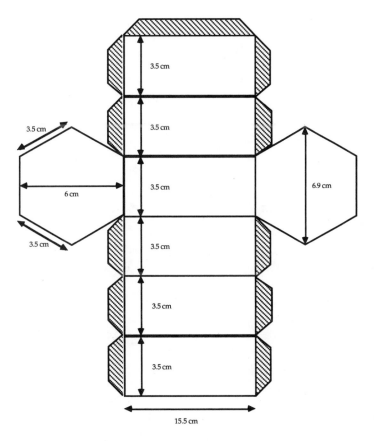

3. The area of cardboard needed for each design (excluding flaps) will be given by the formulas shown below:

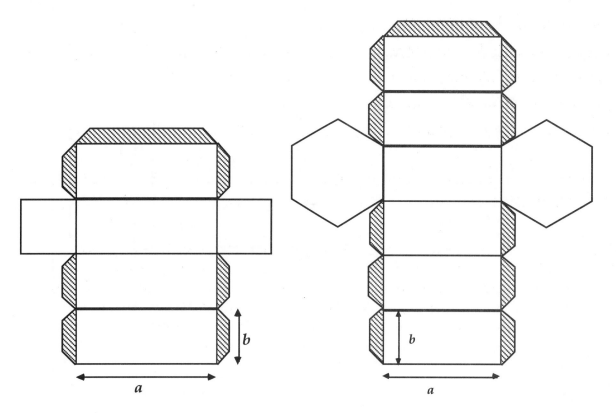

For the rectangular solid, the surface area = 2 b (2a + b).

For the hexagonal box, the surface area = 3 b (2a + √3 b).

When scoring, follow through the student's own measurements.

For the measurements over the page, the rectangular solid has a surface area of 444 cm^2, while the hexagonal box has a surface area of 389 cm^2.

4. A medium level response to this task would just involve dividing the area of the sheet by the area of card used to give an estimate in each case. This may be an optimistic estimate, however, as the nets may not "tessellate" very well, particularly when the flaps are taken into account. A high level response would mention this.

For Formal Assessment

When introducing the task, emphasize the following points:

- students should measure the bottle in centimeters.

- accurate drawings are not required.

- students should explain their reasoning as carefully and as fully as possible.

Allow students to discuss their ideas with at most one partner; discourage pairs from sharing with other pairs.

If any students become completely stuck and need to make models in order to help them visualize the boxes, they may be allowed to do so. A small supply of scissors and glue sticks may be made available for this purpose. Please make it clear to students, however, that the purpose of the task is not to assess model making or accurate drawing and they should not spend longer than is necessary on these activities.

This section offers a characterization of student responses and provides indications of the ways in which the students were successful or unsuccessful in engaging with and completing the task. The descriptions are keyed to the Core Elements of Performance. Our global descriptions of student work range from, "The student needs significant instruction," to, " The student's work meets the essential demands of the task." Samples of student work that exemplify these descriptions of performance are included below, accompanied by commentary on central aspects of each student's response. These sample responses are *representative*; they may not mirror the global description of performance in all respects, being weaker in some and stronger in others.

The characterization of student responses for this task is based on these Core Elements of Performance:

- measure a drawing accurately in centimeters and millimeters.

- use their spatial visualization skills to draw nets of rectangular and hexagonal prisms.

- visualize the way in which the nets will be glued together.

- use the Pythagorean theorem or some trigonometry in solving for the surface area of each net.

- estimate the number of box nets that would fit onto a 1m x 1m sized cardboard.

- justify their computations.

Descriptions of student work

The student needs significant instruction

These papers show evidence of clear understanding of the fact that they need to sketch nets of rectangular and hexagonal boxes, including flaps.

Typically the sketches for both boxes may be correct, but the number or position of flaps may not be correct. The dimensions for the rectangular box may be correct, but the dimensions of the hexagonal box will be inaccurate.

Student A

Student A has drawn sketches of the nets of a rectangular and a hexagonal box. The dimensions of the rectangular box are correct, but an extra flap has been drawn: its surface area has been correctly calculated numerically, but the dimensions shown are linear as is the conversion from centimeters to meters. The dimensions of the sides of the hexagonal box are incorrect.

The student needs some instruction

These papers provide evidence of a clear understanding that there is a need to sketch the nets of a rectangular and a hexagonal box, showing the appropriate dimensions, and to calculate the amount of card needed to make it.

Typically the dimensions of the rectangular box will be correct and the amount of card needed to make this box may be correctly calculated. The dimensions of the hexagonal box will be incorrect.

Student B

Student B has produced a correct net for the rectangular solid box, with flaps shown in suitable places. The net for the hexagonal box, however, is too large as the response assumed that each hexagon will have an edge of 6 cm.

The calculation for the area of card used in the rectangular solid is again correct. The response did not calculate the area of a hexagonal face for the hexagon box.

Student B did not attempt part 4, presumably because the student thought that both of the nets had a larger area than 1 square meter. Looking at the answer to question 3, one can see that the student thinks that there are 100 square cm in a square meter.

The student's work needs to be revised

These papers provide evidence of a clear understanding that there is a need to sketch the nets of a rectangular and a hexagonal box, showing the appropriate dimensions, to calculate the amount of card needed and estimate how many nets can be cut from a sheet of cardboard.

Typically the nets of both prisms are correctly drawn, including the flaps, and the dimensions of both boxes are correctly shown. (The Pythagorean theorem is used to find the dimensions of the hexagonal box.) The amount of card needed to make each prism is calculated, but there may be minor errors. The number of nets which can be cut from a sheet of cardboard is calculated, but no allowance is made for card wasted.

Student C

Student C has correctly drawn sketches of the nets of rectangular and a hexagonal boxes. The dimensions of both boxes are correct and the flaps are correct, if we find it acceptable to have only one flap on the top at the front edge. Although these nets are correct, they are not compact and could be very wasteful of card.

The dimensions of the hexagon are correctly determined using the Pythagorean theorem, and the calculations of the amount of card needed are correct. An estimate of the number of nets which can be made from a sheet of cardboard is made, but no allowance for wastage is made: in this case, the estimate could be very inaccurate.

The student's work meets the essential demands of the task

These papers provide evidence of a clear understanding that there is a need to sketch the nets of a rectangular and a hexagonal box, showing the appropriate dimensions, to calculate the amount of card needed and estimate how many nets can be cut from a sheet of cardboard.

Typically the nets of both boxes are correctly drawn, including flaps, and the dimensions of both boxes are correctly shown. (The Pythagorean theorem is used

to find the dimensions of the hexagonal box.) The amount of card needed to make each box is correctly calculated. The number of nets which can be cut from a sheet of cardboard is calculated and some allowance is made for card wasted. Computations are justified.

Student D

This is a very good response.

Student D has successfully designed the two nets, and has added the glue flaps in sensible places. For the 'square top' net, some of these flaps are 3 cm wide, whereas elsewhere they are 1 cm wide. The necessary dimensions are all present, though for the hexagonal box, some have been left as surds. The response shows real ability at dealing with the dimensions of the hexagon.

The calculations for the area of card are correct and these include the area of the glue flaps. The response has not evaluated the area of the hexagonal net for some reason. (Perhaps there was no calculator available?).

The solution to part 4 is well done. The response has calculated (correctly) the overall dimensions for each net, including the flaps and has then divided each dimension into 100 cm and rounded down. This approach is perhaps not the most efficient as it does not allow for any tessellation of the nets, but it shows a commendable clarity of thought.

Student A

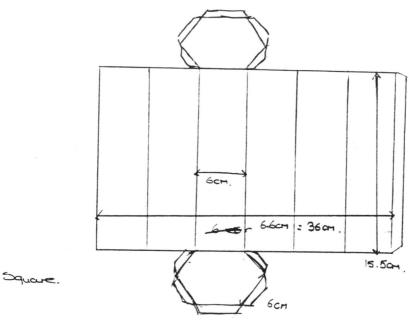

6cm.

6~~cm~~ 6.6cm = 36cm.

15.5cm

Square.

6cm

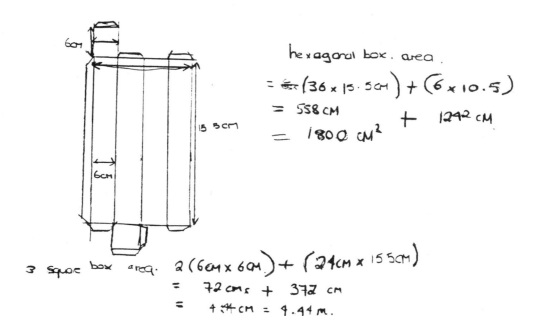

6cm

15.5cm

6cm

hexagonal box. area.

= ~~6x~~ (36 x 15.5cm) + (6 x 10.5)

= 558 CM   + 1242 CM

= 1800 CM²

3 square box area. 2 (6cm x 6cm) + (24cm x 15.5cm)

= 72 cms + 372 cm

= 444 cm = 4.44 m.

SQUARE BOX

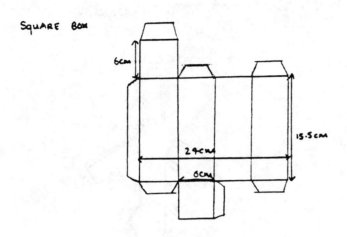

HEXAGONAL BOX

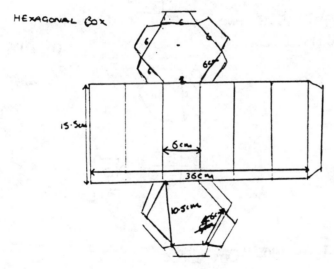

② ⁓

③ Square box area = $2(6cm \times 6cm) + (24cm \times 15.5cm) =$

$\qquad = \quad 72 \quad + \quad 372$

$\qquad = \quad 444 \, cm^2 - 4.44 \, m^2$

Hexagonal box area = $(36 \times 15.5cm) + (6 \times 10.5)2 =$

$\qquad = \quad 558 \qquad + \quad 1242$

$\qquad = \quad 1800 \, cm^2$

Packaging at bottle in a box

1. Rectangular   Hexagonal

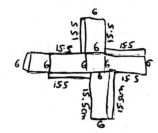 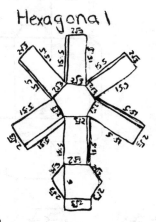

2. Measure of height: 15.5 cm
   measure of width: 6 cm

$(n-2)180$

$(6-2)180 = 720$

$\frac{720}{6} = 120$

$$\frac{3}{\sqrt{3}} = \sqrt{3}$$

$\sqrt{3} \cdot 2 = 2\sqrt{3}$

3. We said each flap was 1cm wide.

"Square Top"

$15.5 \cdot 7 = 108.5$
$108.5 \cdot 4 = 434$
$6 \cdot 7 = 42$
$6 \cdot 6 = 36$
$434 + 42 + 36 = \boxed{512 \, cm^2}$

Hexagonal Top

$15.5 \cdot 2\sqrt{3} = 31\sqrt{3}$
$31\sqrt{3} \cdot 6 = 186\sqrt{3}$
$15.5 \cdot 6 = 93$
$12\sqrt{3} + 12\sqrt{3} = 24\sqrt{3}$
$48\sqrt{3} + 2\sqrt{3}$
$\boxed{236\sqrt{3} + 93 \, cm^2}$

1. $100 \text{ cm}^2 = 10000 \text{ cm}$

$$\frac{10000}{512} = 19$$

$$\frac{10000}{501.7639906} = 19$$

$\sqrt{3} \approx 1.73$

$1.73 \times 236 = 408.28 + 93 = 501.28$

$$\frac{10000}{501.28} = 19$$

You have enough material to make 19 boxes for each of the shapes.

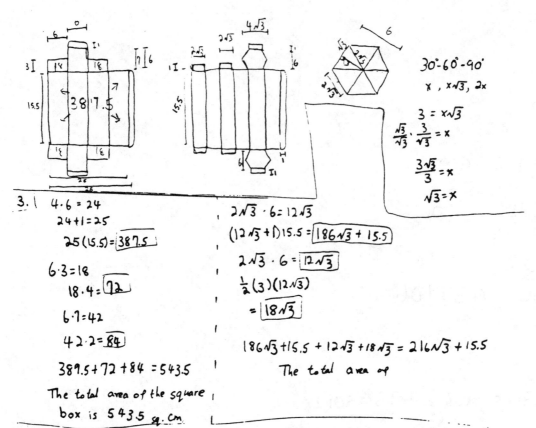

3.1

$4 \cdot 6 = 24$
$24 + 1 = 25$
$25(15.5) = \boxed{387.5}$

$6 \cdot 3 = 18$
$18 \cdot 4 = \boxed{72}$

$6 \cdot 7 = 42$
$42 \cdot 2 = \boxed{84}$

$389.5 + 72 + 84 = 543.5$

The total area of the square box is 543.5 sq. cm

$2\sqrt{3} \cdot 6 = 12\sqrt{3}$
$(12\sqrt{3} + 1)15.5 = \boxed{186\sqrt{3} + 15.5}$
$2\sqrt{3} \cdot 6 = \boxed{12\sqrt{3}}$
$\frac{1}{2}(3)(12\sqrt{3})$
$= \boxed{18\sqrt{3}}$

$186\sqrt{3} + 15.5 + 12\sqrt{3} + 18\sqrt{3} = 216\sqrt{3} + 15.5$

The total area of

$30°-60°-90°$
$x, x\sqrt{3}, 2x$

$3 = x\sqrt{3}$
$\frac{\sqrt{3}}{\sqrt{3}} \cdot \frac{3}{\sqrt{3}} = x$
$\frac{3\sqrt{3}}{3} = x$
$\sqrt{3} = x$

4 When the shapes of the boxes are cut (as shown above), some parts will have to be wasted. Therefore, the longest distances (a, b on the square box & c, d on the hexagonal box) will be the edges of a rectangle that will be cut.

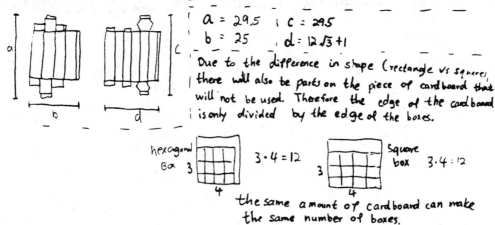

$a = 29.5$ $c = 29.5$
$b = 25$ $d = 12\sqrt{3} + 1$

Due to the difference in shape (rectangle vs square), there will also be parts on the piece of cardboard that will not be used. Therefore the edge of the cardboard is only divided by the edge of the boxes.

hexagonal box   3 $3 \cdot 4 = 12$ Square box $3 \cdot 4 = 12$
                 4   4

the same amount of cardboard can make the same number of boxes.

The "Cross the box" game

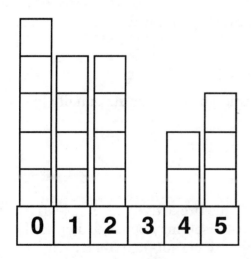 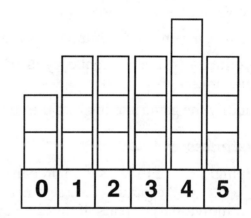

Task Description

Grade Level: High

This task is in three parts.

1. Students follow instructions to play a simple dice game and record the result.

2. Students analyze the game and try to find an optimal strategy for winning.

3. Students adapt the game and try to analyze their new version.

> *Analyze a simple game.*
>
> *Produce a frequency distribution.*
>
> *Count theoretical outcomes.*
>
> *Find a strategy for winning.*
>
> *Modify the game and analyze the new version.*

Assumed Mathematical Background

Students will be expected to have some familiarity with simple dice games.

Core Elements of Performance

This task offers students the opportunity to show that they can:

- follow the rules of a game.

- analyze a game and communicate the results.

- produce an expected frequency distribution by considering equally likely outcomes.

- modify the game and analyze the new situation.

Circumstances

Grouping: Students work in pairs for the pre-activity as they learn the rules of the game. The assessment task itself may be tackled either by individuals or pairs. If the latter approach is adopted, then each member of the pair must produce his or her own written solution.

Materials: Each student has two dice and three coins.
Centimeter squared paper may also be provided.

Estimated time: pre-activity - 20 minutes
assessment task - 45 minutes

The "Cross the box" game

The aim of this assessment is to see how well you can:
- *analyze a simple game.*
- *find and describe a winning strategy.*
- *make up a similar game and analyze it.*

This is a game for two players. You will need two dice and a pencil and paper.
Play through this game once or twice with a partner until you can see how it works.
You will then be asked to analyze the game and modify it.

Setting up the game
Each player draws a shelf labeled 0 through 5.
Each player draws 18 boxes on his or her shelf in piles.
Players can choose how many boxes they put in each pile.
(In the example below, player 1 has put 5 boxes on position 0 and none on position 3.)

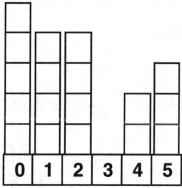   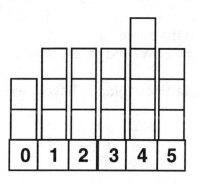

Player 1's shelf   *Player 2's shelf*

Playing the game
Roll the two dice.
Take the smaller score from the bigger score.
Both players cross off one box that is in this position on their shelf.

For example, if you rolled [dice], you calculate 5-3=2 and then
both players cross off one box over position 2 on each shelf like this:

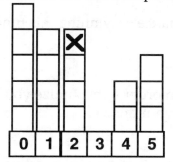   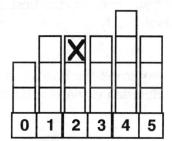

Now roll the dice again and again... up to twenty times.

Aim of the game
The winner is:
either: the first player to cross off *all* of the boxes on their shelf,
or: the player who has crossed off the *most* boxes after 20 rolls of the dice.

---

1. In their first game, Kirsty and Matt set out their boxes as shown below.

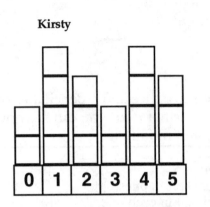

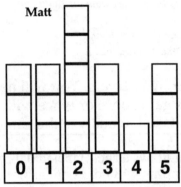

The rolls of the dice were:
(4,2) (5,2) (6,6) (4,3) (1,1) (2,6) (6,2) (5,4) (1,3) (6,1)
(5,6) (2,2) (1,1) (1,5) (1,6) (4,1) (6,5) (5,3) (3,6) (1,2).
(a) Who won the game?
(b) How many boxes did each player cross off?

2. Kirsty and Matt now plan to have a second game. They set out their boxes as   shown below.

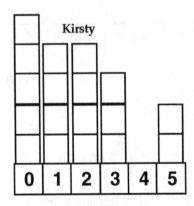

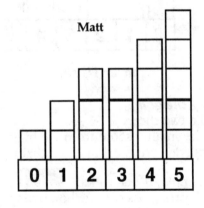

Which player do you think has the best chance of winning this time?
Explain your reasons fully.

3. What is the *best* way to set the boxes out in order to maximize your chances of winning? Give a detailed explanation for your answer.

4. (a) Devise a different version of the game.
    This time use three coins instead of the two dice.
    You decide which boxes to cross off by tossing the coins.
    Write out some new rules for playing the game.

    (b) What is the best way of setting out the boxes to maximize your chances of winning, for your new game?

A Sample Solution

1.   The game finishes as shown below:

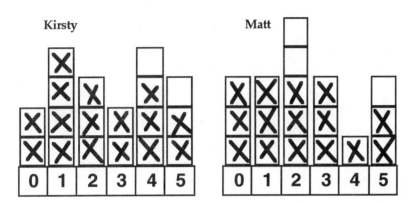

Kirsty wins because she crossed off 16 boxes, while Matt only crossed off 15.

2. & 3. Kirsty should win because she has more 0's, 1's and 2's and fewer 4's and 5's. The following table shows the possible differences when two dice are thrown.

First dice

		1	2	3	4	5	6
	1	0	1	2	3	4	5
Second	2	1	0	1	2	3	4
dice	3	2	1	0	1	2	3
	4	3	2	1	0	1	2
	5	4	3	2	1	0	1
	6	5	4	3	2	1	0

This shows that if a dice is thrown 36 times, the expected frequencies are:

Difference	0	1	2	3	4	5
Expected frequency	6	10	8	6	4	2

The more closely the arrangement of boxes corresponds to this distribution, the better the chance of winning.

As a player must place 18 boxes, she should set the boxes out in the pattern: 3, 5, 4, 3, 2, 1 (where each number is one half the entry in the table).

4. When three coins are tossed, there are eight possible outcomes:

HHH   HHT   HTH   HTT
THH THT   TTH TTT

A similar game would be to play cross the box according to how many Heads are obtained; 0, 1, 2 or 3.

This would give an expected distribution of:

Number of heads	0	1	2	3
Frequency	1	3	3	1

So to maximize the chances of winning, a player should set her boxes out to correspond to this distribution.

For Formal Assessment

A pre-activity

It is important that the students have a clear understanding of the rules of the game before embarking on the assessment task itself.

Page 1 of the prompt and two dice should be issued to each student. Do not issue page 2 of the prompt, which contains the assessment task, at this stage. Read through the rules of the game with the class.

Ask two students to come to the front of the room to play a demonstration game. Invite each to draw a shelf on the board or overhead projector, and to place the 18 boxes where they like. Throw the dice, calculate the difference, and ask each student to put a cross in the box over that position, if one exists. Continue in this way until a winner is declared. (A photocopiable transparency master is provided on the next page.)

Now ask students to play a second game, this time with a partner.

Extensions

You may like to invite students to share their ideas for the coins version of the game and test their winning strategies. Other games may also be suggested and explored. (How about a version with three dice?)

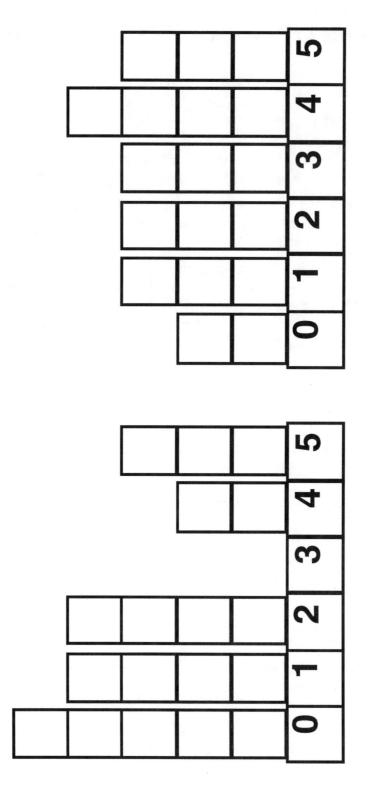

Photocopiable transparency master for pre-activity.

This section offers a characterization of student responses and provides indications of the ways in which the students were successful or unsuccessful in engaging with and completing the task. The descriptions are keyed to the Core Elements of Performance. Our global descriptions of student work range from, "The student needs significant instruction," to, "The student's work meets the essential demands of the task." Samples of student work that exemplify these descriptions of performance are included below, accompanied by commentary on central aspects of each student's response. These sample responses are *representative*; they may not mirror the global description of performance in all respects, being weaker in some and stronger in others.

The characterization of student responses for this task is based on these Core Elements of Performance:

- follow the rules of a game.
- analyze a game and communicate the results.
- produce an expected frequency distribution by considering equally likely outcomes.
- modify the game and analyze the new situation.

Descriptions of student work

The student needs significant instruction

These papers show, at most, evidence that the student has understood the given situation.

Typically, the student has followed the rules in completing question 1, with perhaps a minor error, but has not made any further progress.

Student A

1. Student A's answer shows understanding of the game and the ability to follow the rules.

2&3 The response incorrectly says that Matt has more chance of winning, but does not explain the reasons clearly.

The student needs some instruction

These papers provide evidence that the student has understood the game and begun to analyze the given situation.

Typically, the student has completed question 1 successfully (apart from a minor error) and has correctly identified the player who is most likely to win in question 2, although the reasoning may be incomplete or poorly communicated.

Student B

1. Student B's answer shows an understanding of the game and an ability to follow the rules accurately.

2. The reason for Kirsty being the most likely winner recognizes that 0 through 4 should occur more often than 5. This is correct, as far as it goes. The answer to question 3, however, seems to imply that 4 will occur with the same frequency as 5.

Student C

1. Student C's answer shows an understanding of the game and the ability to follow the rules accurately.

2&3 The answers here seem contradictory. The reason that Matt should win because his boxes are 'more leveled out' contradicts the assertion that 'mainly the dice will land on the middle numbers'. No analysis is produced to support these conclusions.

4. The student has produced an incomplete set of rules for his own game. The response only says what should be done if two heads are thrown. Again there is no analysis.

The student's work needs to be revised

These papers show that the student has understood the game, and has made considerable progress in analyzing the game.

Typically, the student has completed question 1 successfully (apart from a minor error) and has correctly identified the player who is most likely to win in question 2 and has explained the reasons why. The student has also made an analysis of the various possible outcomes obtained when the two dice are thrown and presented this in an organized way for question 3. There may be an error in this analysis such as failing to count (5,1) as different from (1,5).

Student D

1. Student D's answer shows a full understanding of the game and the ability to follow the rules accurately.

2&3 The student believes that lower numbers are easier to obtain than higher numbers and uses this to justify the argument that Kirsty should win. The response now analyzes the possible outcomes carefully and systematically. The response shows an awareness that (4,6) and (6,4), for example, must be treated as separate, equally likely outcomes, but has failed to realize that (6,6) and (6,6) are identical! Apart from this one error, the argument is correct. Student D has now listed 42 outcomes. It is therefore impossible to translate the final distribution into the 18 boxes required, so the student has tried to use an arrangement that approximates to it.

4. The response shows no attempt for question 4.

Student E

1. Student E's answer shows a full understanding of the game and the ability to follow the rules accurately.

2&3   The response begins with an analysis of the outcomes. Unlike Student D, the student has not realized that (4,6) and (6,4) should be counted separately and has so obtained the frequency distribution 6,5,4,3,2,1 instead of 6,10,8,6,4,2. The argument that Kirsty should win is correct, based on the analysis. Interestingly, Student E does not appear to realize that an analysis may be used to obtain the optimal arrangement for the boxes. By chance (?), (or perhaps much evidence is not presented here) the student seems to have hit on the optimal arrangement experimentally. The relative frequency of zeros obtained does not correspond with the analysis, but this goes unnoticed.

4.   Student E's description of the new game is complete, and fairly clear. The student has played one game and recorded the results. There is no theoretical analysis, however, and the student has not realized the symmetry that should exist between heads and tails. Again the response tries to arrive at the optimal placement of boxes by adapting the experimental distribution to the required number of boxes.

The student's work meets the essential demands of the task

Almost all the core elements of performance are demonstrably present.

Typically, the student has completed question 1 successfully (apart from a minor error) and has correctly identified the player who is most likely to win in question 2 and has explained the reasons why. The student has also made an almost correct analysis of the various possible outcomes obtained when the two dice are thrown and presented this in an organized way for question 3. The student has succeeded in designing an alternative version of the game using the three coins, and has begun to analyze this situation. There may be a minor error in the analysis.

Student F

1.   Student F's answer shows full understanding of the rules of the game.

2.   The response correctly analyzes the range of possible outcomes.

3.   On the basis of the analysis, the response suggests two possible arrangements of the boxes and then investigates these experimentally.

4   The student experiments using three coins, recording the number of heads when all three are tossed a number of times. On the basis of the experimental results, the response suggests how the boxes should be set up.

Task 6100

Student A

[

The Cross the box Game

1. The rolls of the dice were:

(2) (3) (0) (1) (6) (4) (4) (1) (2)(5)
(1) (0) (0) (4) (6) (3) (1) (2) (3)(1)

a) The winner after 20 rolls of dice was Kirsty because she had more crosses in the boxes.

b) Kirsty had 16 crosses
Matt had 15 crosses

2, In the second game I believe that Matt has more of a chance of winning because his choice of boxes are evenly set out to give a better ratio on the numbers rolled.

3) The best way to set out the boxes is first of all to find the ratio of the dice (or in by rolling it a number of times. Then according to the ratio even the boxes out accordingly.

4a) On the three coins you have heads and tails on each side and which ever two of the coins get the cross. You have six throws to them which show you mark each one to go in like this. If you have three heads or tails re throw the coins. The winner is the one to fill the boxes first.

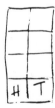

b) See question 3.

The "Cross the Box" Game.

IIII IIII IIII IIII   I WON by 1.

IIII IIII IIII IIII.

I won by 1.

Misses = IIII

KIRSTY.

Misses = IIII

MATT.

a) Kirsty won by 1
b) 16 for kirsty an 15 for Matt.

2, I think kirsty has the best chance of winning the game because a '0' comes up quite alot along with all the others except a '5' which is quite rare.

3, I think the best way to set out the boxes is like .4,4,4,11. so it looks like a very simple 'Postman Pat' van.

The "Cross the box" Game

Kirsty   Matt

Dice Numbers Rolled
(2)(3)(0)(1)(0)(4)(4)(1)(2)(5)
(1)(0)(0)(4)(5)(3)(1)(2)(3)(1)

(a) Kirsty has won the game because she has got 16 boxes ticked off and Matt has only got 15 boxes ticked off.

(b) Kirsty had 16 boxes.
Matt had 15 boxes.

2. In the second game I think that Matt will win because his boxes are more leveled out so it gives him more of a chance.

3. The best way for it is to set out the boxes level. Although mainly the dice will land on the middle number.

4.
(a) You could have two shelves head and tails. When you throw the three dice if you have two heads you cross out a box, under the heads column you have 10 boxes to put in two shelves. You have 15 tosses you can either fill the column or cross out as much boxes as possible.

<u>The "cross the box" Game.</u>

1. (4.2) (5.2) (6.6) (4.3) (1.1) (2.6) (6.2) (5.4) (1.3) (6.1)
   (5.6) (2.2) (1.1) (1.5) (1.6) (4.1) (6.5) (5.3) (3.6) (1.2)
   Are the rolls of the dice.
   a) who won the game? Kirsty.
   b) Kirsty crossed off 16 boxes
      Matt crossed off 15 boxes.

2. ways of working out 0, 1, 2, 3, 4, 5.

   0 = 1-1   1 = 2-1   2 = 3-1   3 = 4-1
   0 = 2-2   1 = 3-2   2 = 4-2   3 = 5-2
   0 = 3-3   1 = 4-3   2 = 5-3   4 = 6-3
   0 = 4-4   1 = 5-4   2 = 6-4
   0 = 5-5   1 = 6-5
   0 = 6-6
      6 ways   5 ways   4 ways   3 ways

   4 = 5-1   5 = 6-1
   4 = 6-2

   2 ways   1 way.

   This shows that you are more likely to get
   a lower number than a higher number.
   Kirsty will probably win because she has
   more lower numbers than higher ones.

3. This the best way to set out the boxes
   in order to maximise your chances of
   winning.

1) 2-2 =0   6) 5-4=1
2) 5-4 =1   7) 4-2=2
3) 5-4 =1   8) 6-5=1
4) 2-1 =1   9) 6-3=3
5) 4-2=2   10) 2-1=1

③ left .

11) 5-3= 2   12) 5-1=4
13) 5-1=4   14) 1-1=0
15) 5-1=4   16) 5-1=4
17) 4-1=3   18) 4-2=2
19) 5-1=4   20) 3-1=2

1) 5-2=3   11) 2-2=0
2) 1-1=0   12) 5-3=2
3) 3-2=1   13) 5-5=0
4) 6-6=0   14) 4-2=2
5) 4-3=1   15) 4-2=2
6) 3-2=1   16) 3-2=1
7) 3-2=1   17) 6-4=2
8) 3-2=1   18) 5-4=1
9) 6-5=1   19) 5-5=0
10) 6-2=4   20) 5-4=1

5 left

our idea was to have lots of boxes for
lower numbers but only a few for the 0.
But this idea didn't really work as you
can see above. we couldn't find the
best way to place the boxes because
it was different every time.

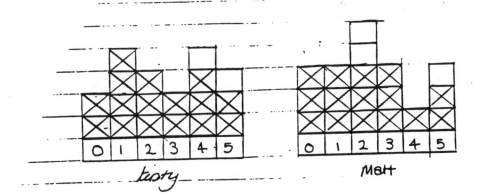

The "cross the box" game

Kirsty   Matt

a) Kirsty won this game.
b) Kirsty crossed off 16 boxes and
   Matt crossed off 15 boxes.

2. We think that Kirsty would have the best chance of
   winning this time because there is more combinations
   for the lower numbers . . .   higher numbers. Matt
   has put 5 boxes on the chance of getting a 5. This is not
   a good idea because there are only two ways of getting
   this (6.1.) and (1.6)

3. The chances of getting 0   The chances of getting 1.

dice 1	dice 2		dice 1	dice 2	
6	6		6	5	
6	6		5	6	
5	5		5	4	
5	5	⑫	4	5	⑩
4	4		4	3	
4	4		3	4	
3	3		3	2	
3	3		2	3	
2	2		2	1	
2	2		1	2	
1	1				
1	1				

The chances of getting 2.		The chances of getting 3	
dice 1	dice 2	Dice 1	Dice 2
6	4	6	3
4	6	3	6
5	3	5	2
3	5 ⑧	2	5 ⑥
4	2	4	1
2	4	1	4
3	1		
1	3		

The chances of getting 4		The chances of getting 5	
Dice 1	Dice 2	Dice 1	Dice 2
6	2	6	1 ②
2	6 ④	1	6
5	1		
1	5		

Number	How many combinations
0	12
1	10
2	8
3	6
4	4
5	2

```
          ┌─┬─┐
          │ │ │
          │ │ │
          │ │ │
      ┌───┼─┼─┤
      │   │ │ │
  ┌───┤   │ │ ├───┐
  │ 0 │ 1 │2│3│4│5│
  └───┴───┴─┴─┴─┴─┘
```

as you go down the table the number 2 is taken off the amount of combinations this proves that the lowest number has the highest combinations.

4. a) 15 is the total amount of boxes.

1) 3 rails
2) 2 head, 1 tail
3) 2 head, 1 tail
4) 3 heads
5) 3 heads
6) 2 heads 1 tail
7) 2 heads 1 tail
8) 2 heads 1 tail

9) 3 heads
10) 2 heads 1 tail
11) 3 heads
12) 3 heads
13) 2 heads 1 tail
14) 2 tails 1 head
15) 2 tails 1 head

what you do is throw the three coins and depending on what is on the coins you mark down on the table.

b) The best way of setting out the boxes is to have more 2 heads and 1 tail.

The "Cross the box" Game

1. The rolls are: (4·2)(5·2)(6·6)(4·3)(1·1)(2·6)(6·2)(5·4)(1·3)(6·1)(5·6)(2·2)
   (1·1)(1·5)(1·6)(4·1)(6·5)(5·3)(3·6)(1·2)

a) Kirsty won the game.

b) Kirsty crossed off 16 boxes
   Matt crossed off 15 boxes

2. I think Kirsty has a better chance because there are more
   ways of getting low numbers than high.

Ways of working it out

0=1-1	1=2-1	2=3-1	3=4-1	4=2-2	5=6-1
0=2-2	1=3-2	2=4-2	3=5-2	4=6-4	
0=3-3	1=4-3	2=5-3	3=6-3		
0=4-4	1=5-4	2=6-4			
0=5-5	1=6-5				
0=6-6					

3. This is the best way of setting the boxes out in order to
   maximise your chances of winning.

Our idea was to have more boxes on 1 and 2 than on the
higher numbers. We tried these two ways and found the
first was better.

4. PTO

15 is the total amount of boxes.

a)

X			
X	X		
	X	X	X
	X	X	
	X	X	

1 head   2 heads   3 heads   3 tails
2 tails   1 tail

1) 3 tails   6) 2 heads   11) 3 heads
2) 2 heads   7) 3 heads   12) 3 heads
3) 2 heads   8) 2 heads   13) 2 heads
4) 3 heads   9) 3 heads   14) 2 tails.
5) 3 heads   10) 2 heads   15) 2 tails

You shake 3 coins out then mark the box that is correct for your result.

b)

2 tails	3 heads	3	3
1 head	1 tail	heads	tails

This is the best way of setting out the boxes to maximise the chances of winning

Wheelchair access

Task Description

Grade Level: High

Students are told that wheelchair access is required for a viewing platform that is 11 feet high. The ramp must conform to the specifications of the Americans with Disabilities Act.

> **Select and use the concept of slope.**
>
> **Interpret specifications.**

Assumed Mathematical Background

Students should have completed some work with the concept of slope thought of as the (vertical) rise divided by the horizontal run.

Core Elements of Performance

- Use the concept of slope in the setting of a wheelchair ramp.
- Interpret the specifications and constraints of the American with Disabilities Act.

Circumstances

Grouping:	Students work in pairs.
Materials:	materials to build the ramp
Estimated time:	45 minutes

Wheelchair access

In this task you are asked to design a ramp to give wheelchair access to a viewing platform.
You are given the height of the platform, and requirements that all wheelchair ramps must meet.

Wheelchair access is needed for a viewing platform which is 10 feet above the ground.
There is available a square area 45 feet on a side in which a ramp is to be built.
The ramp must comply with the Americans with Disabilities Act regulations that are
given below.

Draw a diagram to show how you have created the access.

Communicate clearly your design decisions: how many sections are there, and what
size?

Include your calculations.

Show how each specification is met.

The Americans with Disabilities Act specifications

- **The maximum slope that a wheelchair ramp can have is " one in twelve".**
- **No one section of the ramp can rise more than 30 inches.**
- **Higher rises are created by joining two sections with a horizontal landing
  60 inches long.**
- **A ramp must have a 60 inch landing at the beginning and end.**
- **The width of a ramp must be 72 inches.**

Scale: $\frac{1}{4}$ inch represents 1 foot.

Total of five linked ramps.

About this task

Many students found this task challenging. Communicating the solution is one of its more challenging aspects. If at all possible, encourage students to make a model ramp as a solution, and this will give students a means to communicate effectively this complex structure. Useful materials that can be used to make a ramp are paper or cardboard.

This section offers a characterization of student responses and provides indications of the ways in which the students were successful or unsuccessful in engaging with and completing the task. The descriptions are keyed to the Core Elements of Performance. Our global descriptions of student work range from, "The student needs significant instruction," to, " The student's work meets the essential demands of the task." Samples of student work that exemplify these descriptions of performance are included below, accompanied by commentary on central aspects of each student's response. These sample responses are *representative*; they may not mirror the global description of performance in all respects, being weaker in some and stronger in others.

The characterization of student responses for this task is based on these Core Elements of Performance:

- Use the concept of slope in the setting of a wheelchair ramp.

- Interpret the specifications and constraints of The American with Disabilities Act.

Descriptions of student work

The student needs significant instruction

These papers show at most evidence that the student has a clear understanding of at least one of the constraints.

Student A

This response shows that the student formulates the problem as that of determining the number of 30 inch ramps needed to reach a height of 120 inches. The response does not show us that the know how to construct slopes that conform to the specifications of the ADA.

The student needs some instruction

These papers provide evidence that the student has some understanding of slope.

Student B

This response shows that it can construct a ramp with the required slope. The student has interpreted the constraints but has difficulty orienting the ramp so that it fits into the given space.

The student's work needs to be revised

These papers show that the student has essentially accomplished the task. The work could be revised to perfection.

Student C

This student has difficulty communicating the work that has been carried out. The construction of a model would help the student to show how each of the constraints has been met.

The student's work meets the essential demands of the task

The student ensures that each constraint is met and fully accomplishes the task.

Student D

This response presents a model that is made with paper. The darker lines indicate where the paper has been cut to make a model ramp.

Student A

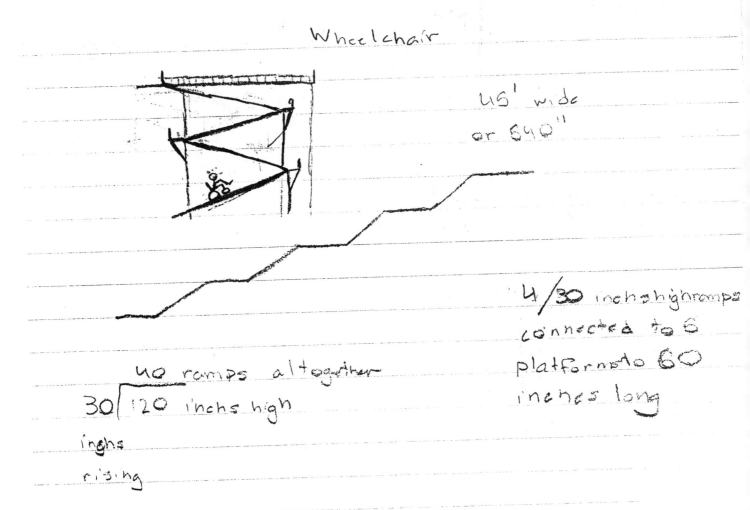

Wheelchair

45' wide
or 540"

4/30 inchs high ramps
connected to 6
platforms to 60
inches long

40 ramps altogether
30) 120 inchs high

inghs
rising

10ft = 120in
45ft = 540in

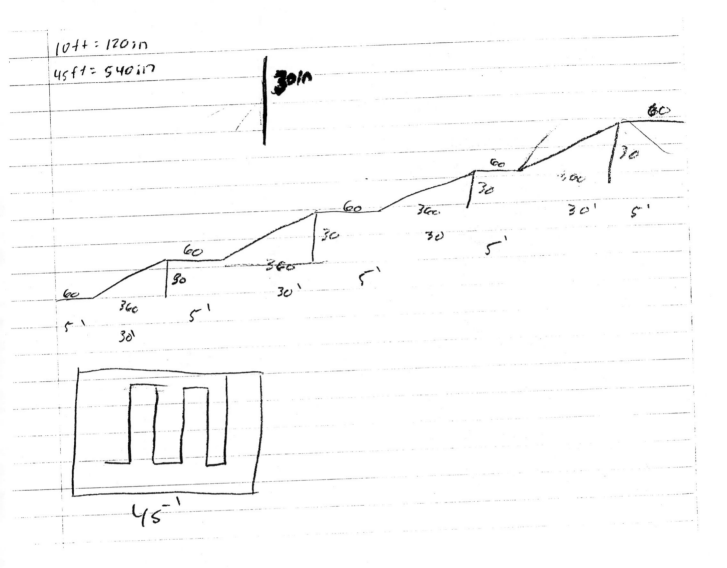

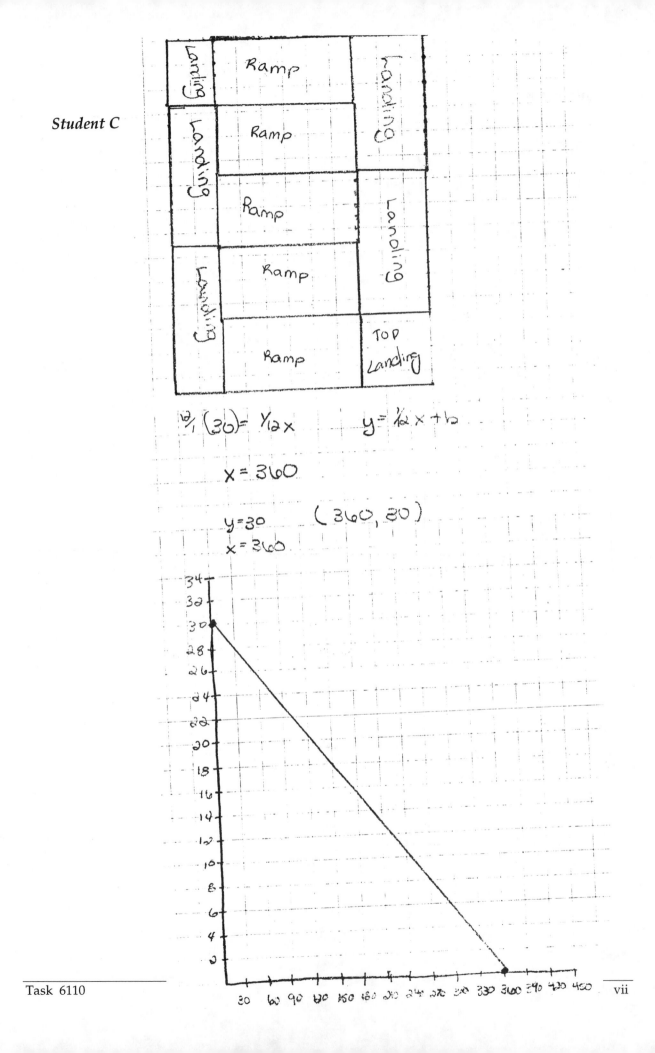

Student C

Landing | Ramp

Landing | Ramp

Landing | Ramp | Landing

Landing | Ramp

Landing | Ramp | TOP Landing

$$\frac{12}{1}(30) = \frac{y}{12}x$$

$$y = \frac{1}{12}x + b$$

$$x = 360$$

$$y = 30 \qquad (360, 20)$$
$$x = 360$$

Student D

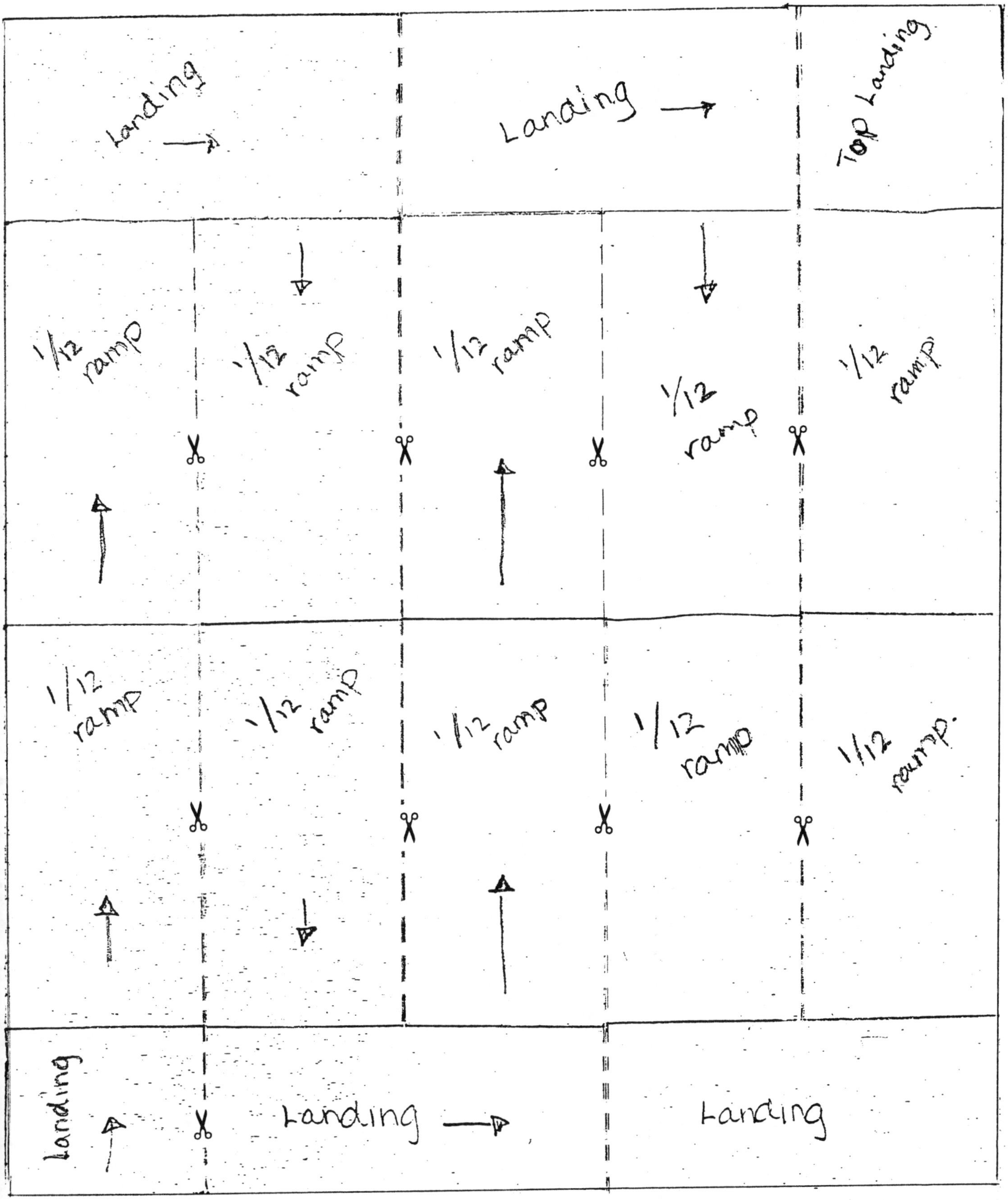
Landing
Landing
Top Landing
1/12 ramp
1/12 ramp
1/12 ramp
1/12 ramp
1/12 ramp
1/12 ramp
1/12 ramp
1/12 ramp
1/12 ramp
1/12 ramp.
Landing
Landing
Landing